A holiday in the mou
sounds beyond Jason Wright's wildest dreams! But within twenty-four hours of arriving as guest of his friend Colonel Chula, whom he had helped foil a terrorist hijacking over Thailand three months earlier, the dream turns into a nightmare.

Jason and Angus Bain, a journalist, stumble across a drug-smuggling route used by Shan rebels for money to buy arms to use in their fight for independence. Jason and Angus are seized, along with two young archaeologists working nearby, and taken as hostages across the border into Burma, where a huge consignment of heroin is waiting to be run into Thailand.

But this lawless area holds other armed bands, all more or less involved in the illegal opium trade, and they too have their eyes on the heroin. Battle, murder and treachery follow it across the forested mountains, and the hostages find they must summon all their resolution and cunning if they are to survive.

This is an exciting book for older Puffin readers who will enjoy both the unusual setting and the highly topical subject. Jason Wright's earlier adventure, *Hijacked!*, is also available as a Puffin.

James Marks (a pseudonym) was born in China in 1921, of Scottish parents, and was educated in Scotland. He joined the Argyll and Sutherland Highlanders in 1940 while studying Veterinary Science at Glasgow University. Commissioned in 1941, he spent the next seven years as a platoon and company commander, serving in the Burma campaign and Java. After several years in Malaya, Nepal and Tibet, he resigned his commission and started a plantation in the North Borneo Highlands with his wife and two children but local politics brought difficulties, so he moved to Australia. He now lives in Scotland.

*Another book by J. M. Marks*

HIJACKED!

# J. M. MARKS

# BORDER KIDNAP

*Illustrated by Robert Gibson*

PUFFIN BOOKS

*in association with Oxford University Press*

Puffin Books, Penguin Books Ltd, Harmondsworth, Middlesex, England
Viking Penguin Inc., 40 West 23rd Street, New York, New York 10010, U.S.A.
Penguin Books Australia Ltd, Ringwood, Victoria, Australia
Penguin Books Canada Limited, 2801 John Street, Markham, Ontario, Canada L3R 1B4
Penguin Books (N.Z.) Ltd, 182–190 Wairau Road, Auckland 10, New Zealand

—

First published as *The Triangle* by Oxford University Press 1974
Revised and published in Puffin Books 1979
Reprinted 1986

—

Copyright © J. M. Marks, 1974, 1979
Illustrations copyright © Robert Gibson, 1974
All rights reserved

—

Made and printed in Great Britain
by Richard Clay (The Chaucer Press) Ltd,
Bungay, Suffolk
Set in Monotype Baskerville

# CONTENTS

## I

## FOREST CAMP

'THERE!' shouted the pilot above the noise of the
engine. 'Ban Phao!' He swung the light Cessna in a
long banking turn over the valley and pointed: 'There,
just below us now. See it?'

From the passenger seat Jason craned to see down
past a wing strut. At first he made out only the green
and yellow patchwork of dry rice fields in their valley
among the mountains, but then he spotted the village
itself – a double row of thatched houses lining a single

wide street, a thread of track leading from it to an oblong of paler green, the landing strip. 'Got it!'

The Thai pilot grinned. 'Pretty remote place for a holiday! But I'll take you round a bit first, show you the country.'

He kicked the rudder, tilted the control column and the aircraft banked again above a steep ridge bordering the valley. Broken water showed white in the depths of a gorge, and pointing north across it to the blue-green mountains beyond the pilot shouted: 'Burma that side – Shan States!' He flew east along the ridge for a minute or two, then prodded Jason and pointed down: 'Mekong!'

South past the end of the ridge flowed a bronze and silver river, and Jason gasped, for it was nearly half a mile wide. On the far bank low hills stood up, rising to yet more mountains behind, and the pilot shouted: 'Laos!' He grimaced and shook a warning hand, 'Communist country – we don't want to come down there!' and swung the plane hard round.

As they flew back to Ban Phao Jason looked north once more into Burma, at the forested ridges rising thousands of feet, at the scattered clearings all apparently growing the same white-flowered crop, and at the hill-top villages. It was wild country across there.

Then the pilot prodded him again, and pointed down at a group of figures at the edge of the landing strip: 'Colonel Chula!'

From the plexiglass window Jason waved down at the foreshortened, rather thickset figure standing with a slimmer second man in front of the group of uniformed police. Yes, there he was all right – Colonel Chulananda

Sirikachon, Deputy Minister of Home Affairs of the
Kingdom of Thailand, his host for this unusual holiday
and his companion and ally in that desperate aircraft
hijacking in which Jason had been caught up only three
short months before.

'Going down!' The Cessna seemed to pause in the
air as they throttled back, the ground came up to meet
them – and then they were down and bumping rapidly
along the grassy strip. They slowed, turned and taxied
back with a noisy sputtering of engine and stopped and
switched off a few yards from the waiting vehicles.

'Okay,' said the pilot, his voice loud in the sudden
quiet. He leaned back, unbuckling his harness, and
worked his shoulders. 'Have a good holiday in the
Triangle.' He grinned rather ruefully. 'For me, it's
straight back to Bangkok with a passenger.'

'Oh, that's a bit hard!' commiserated Jason. 'Not
even a night up here in the cool?'

'No such luck. Perhaps in ten days, when I pick you
up again.'

'Right: see you then. And thanks for the ride!' He
gave the pilot a quick wink, slipped out of his safety
harness, seized his suitcase and jumped down to greet
the stocky figure in khaki shirt and shorts striding across
to meet him.

'Jason!' There was no mistaking the warmth of
Colonel Chula's welcome, and Jason looked at him
with a rush of affection. His last sight of the Colonel had
been from a helicopter taking off from beside the wreck
of the hijacked airliner, when Chula, his black hair
blowing wildly in the downward blast of the rotors,
had called up to him: 'You will hear from me!' He

had been as good as his word, and now Jason was his guest for the great Songkran festival in the normally forbidden border zone of Northern Thailand – a holiday beyond his wildest dreams.

'How was the journey, Jason – and Bangkok, were you properly looked after on your arrival from school in England?'

'Oh, yes, Sir – everything was super, thanks.' Jason looked round rather shyly. From the respectful attitudes of the armed police who stood by the two field cars and the smart salute the pilot gave as he came over to report it was only too clear that Colonel Chula was a man of considerable authority.

'We will now go to the forest camp, Jason, your home for the next few days while we attend the various ceremonies and perhaps tour the area a little. Have you ever seen elephants working? No? But first,' he extended a hand to the dapper figure behind him, 'you must meet Mr Varalak Sirikachon, of the United Nations Department of Education and Cultural Affairs. He is returning to Bangkok after one of his official visits up here.'

'Mr Sirikachon?' repeated Jason, questioningly, and the other man smiled: 'Ah! – you noticed the name! Yes, Colonel Chula and I are related; we are actually second cousins.' His English was faultless, and Jason looked at him with interest. Where the bulky Chula, short-haired and smoking a large cigar, was carelessly dressed in rather creased khaki, Varalak wore immaculately tailored Bedford cord slacks and raw-silk shirt, smoked a cigarette in a carved ivory holder, and his fashionably long hair, greying somewhat at the temples, was brushed back carefully almost to his collar.

'So you are Jason Wright!' Varalak spoke warmly. 'I have been looking forward so much to meeting you. I heard something from my cousin about how well you behaved during that hijack down in Pattani.' Jason stiffened. Had Colonel Chula talked too much? 'Three days in that hot aircraft must have been a great ordeal,' went on the older man, and Jason relaxed once more. It was clear that Chula had let slip nothing about Jason's escape from the plane or his connection with the death of the first hijacker.

'You are, perhaps, fifteen years of age? I was under the impression that you were somewhat older,' mused Varalak, his eyes observant, but then he laughed. 'Anyway, my cousin said that you deserved a better impression of our country than your first arrival in a hijacked airliner! I trust this is an improvement?'

'Oh, yes.' Jason agreed with a grin. 'This is very different. But you must be sorry to have to go back, Mr Sirikachon. Have you had a long stay?'

'Just a day or two, Jason. But I do manage occasional trips up here – two young compatriots of yours are making really interesting archaeological discoveries in this border area. That comes under my particular department, so' – he laughed gently – 'I am able to make occasional visits and combine business with pleasure! But I must be off.' He held out his hand once more. 'Enjoy your stay, Jason, and don't overdo the celebrations! Perhaps we will meet again, and you can tell me how you spent your time.' He nodded, exchanged a quick word in Thai with Colonel Chula, carefully extinguished his cigarette, beckoned to the pilot and set off briskly towards the aircraft.

They waved goodbye as the Cessna took off and climbed south out of the valley, then Colonel Chula turned to Jason with a broad smile: 'Now, Jason, we can begin our holiday.'

Talking busily, like old friends, they walked towards the jeep. 'You have had a long journey, Jason,' said the Colonel, 'but I hope that you will find it worth while.' He paused while Jason jumped into the back and himself sat beside the driver, nodded to him, and turned to Jason again as they drove off. 'Now, how are your parents? Both well? Good. And are you making progress at school? I seem to remember your father telling me in Bangkok that you were to sit some examinations that same month. Did you find these difficult?'

'They weren't too easy!' Jason grinned in some embarrassment, remembering the very mixed bag of comments on his results.

'Ah, well,' said Colonel Chula philosophically, 'you will be able to forget them for a few days. First,' he explained, 'you will have ten days up here, then I thought you might like to see our new Thai holiday resort at Pattaya. It is,' his eyes crinkled in a smile, 'back down south towards your Hijack Beach, but it is a really beautiful place, and the swimming, I am told, is very good. How does that sound to you?'

'It sounds wonderful!'

They drove along the winding track into Ban Phao and a chicken or two fluttered squawking away from their wheels as they entered the outskirts of the little town – for, Jason saw, what had seemed just a village from five thousand feet now appeared quite a respectable township. Although there was only one main street, tiny crooked alleyways ran outwards from it between the shop houses, and all were busy with people. The customers in the open-fronted shops were obviously hill folk; there was no mistaking the Mongoloid features, the black clothing and silver ornaments, the varying and complicated hair styles, and the generally wilder look. Compared with them the Thai and Chinese shopkeepers and market traders looked urban and – curiously – rather out of place. Chula caught his glance: 'Many mountain people have come down for the festival – even some from across the border.' He waved a hand. 'They are busy buying goods to save travel during the rainy season.'

Driving carefully to avoid yet more chickens and the occasional groups squatting around a prospective purchase – including one interested crowd watching a child having a tooth pulled by an itinerant dentist – they crawled in low gear along the main street. At the far end the driver changed gear and increased speed, and Colonel Chula waved at a larger wooden house set on piles amid clumps of purple bougainvillea. 'Rest House – useful for travellers.' He settled back in his seat, then suddenly sat forward and spoke to the driver, who nodded and turned in to the wide, grass-grown drive. Jason looked round and Colonel Chula said briefly: 'Some new arrival; I will just see exactly who it is.'

By the front steps stood a very dusty jeep, and on the verandah rail above rested a pair of well-worn brogue shoes pale with the same dust. Their driver pulled up beside the jeep, the Colonel said to Jason: 'Please wait here,' and ran up the steps.

Watching and listening from below Jason saw the feet swing away from the verandah rail and clump down firmly on to the wooden floor, the basketwork chair creaked and a lean man with short black hair, light grey eyes and blue-black shadow on chin and jaw stood up and held out his hand. 'Good afternoon, Colonel; I had no idea you were up here.' The voice was precise and the accent very faintly Scots.

Chula took the outstretched hand and shook it formally. 'Good afternoon, Mr Bain. You have come far from your base. When did you leave Bangkok?'

'The day before yesterday, Colonel. The roads are better than on my last visit two years ago; a little dusty still, but not bad.'

'And may I ask what brings the Bangkok representative of Amalgamated Press International all the way up here? Surely it is not our local celebrations for the Songkran festival!'

'No, Colonel,' replied Bain crisply. 'I am hoping to gather background material for an article on the Triangle. There is little of interest in the capital at the moment – or anywhere else in South-East Asia. Everyone is just waiting for the rains.'

The Triangle? Jason pricked up his ears. It sounded familiar, somehow, though he could not place it.

'You are too far east for any Triangle activities, Mr Bain – you know that!' The faintest edge crept into Colonel Chula's voice. 'You must have heard something?'

'I have heard nothing, Colonel!'

'But your journalist's nose twitches, eh?' Chula
smiled. 'Well, you will find nothing here, and remember, please – the restricted zone begins just beyond Ban
Phao.' Colonel Chula turned away, but half-way down
the steps called back: 'There is always the Laceys and
Nakhon Wat! If you did an article on that you would
not have completely wasted your time!'

'Thank you, Colonel.' Bain spoke equably. 'I might
just do that.' He walked forward to the verandah rail
to watch the Colonel go down and for the first time
caught sight of Jason, seated below in the jeep. An eyebrow rose fractionally, he started to say something but
checked himself and stood silently watching as the
driver started up and they drove back out on to the
main track.

A phrase from that exchange had intrigued Jason,
and he asked, 'Who are the Laceys, Colonel?'

'They are a brother and sister who are doing some
archaeological work not far from here, at a site called
Nakhon Wat. They think it may turn out to be the
legendary city of Prince Suthon, ruler of Nakhon, long
thought to be a purely mythical figure.'

'They're English, are they?'

'Yes, and they make a useful team. Peter Lacey is an
archaeologist, but his sister, Miss Lacey, is a botanist,
a valuable asset in Asia, where crops and soil conditions
have had so much effect on development. But I am
afraid we will not have time to visit them,' he said with
regret. 'Too much to do here!'

A few minutes of fast, bumpy driving brought them
to the end of the valley road and they slowed abruptly

as the driver changed into four-wheel drive and they began to climb. The track snaked steeply upwards through huge forest trees, occasionally looping back on itself to gain height, in hairpin bends so tight that the driver had continually to back and swing his vehicle hard round – often uncomfortably close to the outer edge.

Looking back through the trees Jason caught glimpses of the valley, well below them now, and already the air seemed cooler. This, he recognized, must be the long ridge above which he had flown so swiftly and easily less than an hour before. Then the ridge – like the village of Ban Phao – had seemed quite small; as they crawled uphill in the jeep, however, he saw that it was a massive wall of hill, almost of mountain, which, together with the gorge beyond, formed the barrier between Thailand and Burma.

There was much to see along the frontier ridge. Hill birds with bright plumage flew up from the lower branches as they passed; other, heavier birds like reddish pheasants scuttled away along the ground, and once a troop of gibbons swung above them with a sound like a strong wind in the tree-tops, till they suddenly lost interest and swung away with wild, whooping calls.

A party of hill people padding downhill along the track stopped to stare, their eyes fastening on Jason in silent wonder. They wore black clothing, the women with their hair elaborately woven in plaits half concealed beneath helmet-like head-dresses of linked silver coins, with gorgets of more coins on neck and breast – all as well as the heavy, cone-shaped baskets carried on their backs and held by head-bands of woven cane.

In his turn Jason looked at them with fascination, at the chain mail of silver, and in particular at the embroidered blue leggings the women wore from their bare feet to the knee. Seeing his stare Colonel Chula said: 'Akha tribespeople. We are on the eastern edge of their lands.'

'Those leggings,' Jason commented. 'I've never seen anyone wear those before!'

Colonel Chula laughed. 'They were originally against jungle thorns,' he said. 'Then the Akha ladies began to ornament them – and now they are part of their dress, whether there are thorns or not.' He chuckled. 'You will find, Jason, that ladies are much the same everywhere – sooner or later they will embroider everything! But you will see many Akhas at our forest camp, as well as the other hill people.' He looked at his watch. 'Not long now, soon we will be over the ridge, and it is just a little way down, in a clearing on the far side.' He fell silent, for it had been an effort to talk against the straining engine's deep growl and the varying pitch as the driver changed from first to second gear and back. Then, with a last few minutes of engine roar, they topped the ridge and drove down the track on the far side.

'Here we are, Jason – the camp!'

They pulled up at the edge of a wide circle of newly built huts of bamboo, log and thatch, set round a clearing on the out-thrust spur of the hillside. The undergrowth had been slashed down and Akha women were raking up the leaves and twigs and cut stems and piling them on fires burning briskly at one end.

'How fine!' Jason sprang from the jeep and took a

deep breath of the mountain air. Colonel Chula watched
with a faint smile as Jason looked about him, eyes
sparkling. The sharp afternoon sunlight, the tangy blue
wood-smoke, the huge trees growing down the slopes
and the distant roar of the river in its gorge below had
an almost Alpine feel.

'Well?' said Colonel Chula, still smiling.

Jason slowly swung his head in admiration. 'It's
great,' he said, unable to find adequate expression for
his feelings, 'just great!'

'Tea,' said the Colonel, 'let us have some tea. It will
refresh you after your journey. We will now go to our
small mess, and afterwards you will have a mountain
shower.'

The mess was a longer building than the individual
huts, its walls of woven bamboo open for a foot or two
under the eaves of the thatched roof to give a panoramic
view north out over the gorge and across into Burma.
A second Thai rose as they entered and Colonel Chula
introduced him as 'Mr Udom'. Jason looked at him
with a quick wary interest as they shook hands, for
Udom was a leaner man than the bulky Chula, his face
sunburned to a dark copper and with the smooth gleam
of days spent in long, hard exercise. Jason wondered for
a moment just what this exercise might be.

'Mr Udom is helping with our arrangements,'
explained Colonel Chula. 'He is very knowledgeable
about our hill peoples.'

Quite obviously not understanding a word of English
but gathering that the Colonel was explaining his
presence Udom smiled and bowed, but noting the
hard expression which the smile only briefly replaced,

Jason thought to himself that Udom did not look at all like an administrator concerned with minor village and tribal affairs. Could he have begun as a policeman? Jason hesitated: in a film Udom would have looked like the gangster! Then the orderly brought tea – plain, weak, without milk or sugar – and Jason sipped it gratefully, forgetting his momentary fancies about Udom, remembering instead the relief with which he had drunk the tea given him by Colonel Chula at their first meeting three months before.

Over tea Colonel Chula outlined their programme: it would include a trip on horseback to see one of the hill villages, fishing with rod and line in the Kwan ('Big mahseer await you there, Jason!') and finally a night of dancing by the hill tribes assembling for the festival. 'We have many different tribes in this border area,' explained the Colonel, 'mainly Akha, Lahu, Lesu, and some Haus. Here in Amphur Mae Chan – that is, the Mae Chan district – Akha predominate; you will recognize them by the silver head-dress worn by the women. The women – who do all the real work – are much more colourful than the men, who wear simply black clothing. They are an interesting people,' he went on reflectively. 'They are really newcomers to the area.'

'When did they come?' Jason asked the question in some surprise. He had assumed that the hill peoples were the original inhabitants, and to his astonishment Colonel Chula said: 'This century. Their real home was Yunnan, but they suffered much at the hands of the Chinese armies that roamed the area after the break-up of the Manchu Empire, so they migrated. First they

travelled south from Yunnan to Kengtung in the Shan
States, then gradually wandered south again over the
mountains into Thailand. The same is true of the other
hill peoples, though the time scale is different. With
strife everywhere the peoples are still on the move,
Jason.' He shook his head in sympathy. 'They search
for a place where they can live their own lives without
oppression. We hope those on our side of the border
have found it. But come.' He rose, dismissing the
subject. 'You will want to have your shower before it
is too dark.'

At a word the orderly ran up with soap and a huge
towel, and Jason followed Colonel Chula out down
through the camp and the groups of working Akhas
along a freshly cleared path down the slope towards a
mountain stream. 'Here you are, Jason,' he said, 'our
camp shower-bath. I am afraid that there are no hot
taps! Let us meet at the mess when you are ready.'

The camp shower was a log pier sticking out into the
water and screened by a partition of split bamboo. A few
yards upstream the water had been dammed by logs,
and from this dam stuck out a bamboo pipe, gushing
a jet of icy water. Jason kicked off his sandals and strip-
ped, noticing that the late afternoon wind was beginning to be just a trifle too fresh for comfort. He sucked
in his breath: it really was very chilly, hopping about
on one foot, his chest roughened by gooseflesh, and now
that he was stark naked the water gushing remorselessly
from the bamboo spout looked colder than ever. He
took a deep breath, stepped forward – and half gasped,
half cried out as the four-inch jet of water struck him
between the shoulder blades. Its force took him by sur-

prise, choking back his grunt of shock and dismay. He hissed, shivering, tempted to give up, to seize his towel, to abandon his bath – but no, he must stick it out! He set his teeth and reached for the soap – but when he stepped away from the jet of water to lather himself the wind searched him out through the interstices of the matting wall, so that it was almost a relief to step under the water again. At last, numb and hissing with cold, he finished, and rubbing water from his eyebrows stepped hastily away from that merciless jet and reached for the towel. He rubbed his face and hair, expecting to shiver until he was dressed – when suddenly he found that his gooseflesh had gone. He stopped his rubbing and looked down; his chest glowed pink, he was warm and steaming, the wind no longer cold. He dressed and stepped out – and there were the Akhas busy working away. None of them gave the slightest sign that they knew of his existence, yet he knew that they had been watching, and he grinned to himself in relief. Just as well he hadn't backed out!

Pulling on a jersey he walked up to the mess, to find his host waiting for him outside.

'Well, Jason?' Was there the faintest gleam of approval in Colonel Chula's eyes. 'Did you enjoy your shower?'

'Perhaps not straight off,' Jason admitted, and for the first time that day saw Chula laugh out loud.

Just below the camp a rocky outcrop gave a superb view out over the hillside, here falling away in steepening cliffs down to the gorge. Beyond, the Burmese peaks glowed green as jade in the light fading from the west, accentuating the white of the strange flowers in the scattered clearings on the ridges. Colonel Chula stood staring down at the gorge, where the white-rimmed water followed the line of the ridge back till it turned north and west into Burma.

'It flows from the mountains where Shans and Burmese meet,' he said reflectively, 'a troubled place.' Before Jason could question him Chula turned and spoke almost gaily: 'But we must not think of politics when Songkran approaches! Anyway, it is getting late.'

That evening they dined on Thai food, beginning with grilled catfish ('caught today down in the Kwan gorge'), the vegetables garnished with pepper sauces. This was quickly followed by an onion omelette of enormous size which Colonel Chula deftly sliced into three with a razor-sharp kitchen knife provided by the cook. Jason was beginning to think that they could ease off, when the Colonel said, with again just the sug-gestion of a smile: 'Good, Jason, I am happy to see that you have an appetite. Now we will examine the main course.'

'The main course?' repeated Jason foolishly. He blinked at the table, now swept clear of the cluttered debris of the giant omelette and the skeleton of the fish.

'Yes, curried chicken. Our cook has been busy pre-paring this ever since we received the signal that your aircraft had taken off for Ban Phao this morning.' He clapped his hands and the servant acknowledged with a word in Thai and whisked out. 'Yes, the cook is very thorough. He takes care to bring just the right in-gredients for the curry paste.' Chula smiled: 'The only heavy bit of equipment we brought up from Bangkok for our tour was his stone block and roller. It is made from what the English call granite, and,' he smiled, 'it causes some discussion whenever we take it. It is exceedingly heavy. But,' he shrugged, 'we had a simple choice: no stone, no cook.'

Jason sat listening to all this with an attentive smile and a sinking heart. That omelette, the fish, those grilled and spicy vegetables – how he regretted his enthusiasm! He'd never manage the cook's pièce de résistance – and if he faltered, if he showed weakness, the cook would be hurt to the depths of his soul. Jason drew a deep breath: he'd eat whatever was offered, if it killed him! But the chicken when it came was delicious, and Jason was finally able to lean back in his chair with the plates empty before him. 'What a meal,' he sighed.

Coffee was served and then the silent Udom, with a brief word in Thai to Colonel Chula, bowed goodnight to Jason and vanished into the darkness. For a moment the conversation languished, the Colonel sipping at his brandy-and-water and Jason at his coffee. Then he remembered something that had once or twice given him cause for uneasy thought. 'I'd always meant to ask you, Sir – where did you find Yasuno?'

'The leader of the hijack gang?' Chula drew reflectively on his cheroot. 'It is interesting that you should ask. We never did find his body.'

'What!' Jason looked at him in dismay. 'But we always thought that the gang –'

'– had all been accounted for? We certainly announced that to the press – and the other four Japanese hijackers were indeed all killed or captured.'

'But if Yasuno was not found –' Jason once again

felt that flicker of unease, but this time it was sharper.

Colonel Chula leant forward and gripped his shoulder. 'You must not worry, Jason! We are convinced that he was swept out to sea and drowned. No one could have survived that storm for very long!'

Jason, although not altogether convinced, felt some reassurance. After all, it had been three months since the hijack – and surely Yasuno would have been spotted by someone if he had survived!

'I still think, however, that it would be prudent for the part you played to be kept secret,' said the Colonel. 'It is a pity, but it could be dangerous for you if it were known.' He rose. 'Now, it is time for us all to sleep. Tomorrow we have a busy day.'

Snug in his blankets Jason slept soundly, never moving till dawn crept in through below the thatch. Warm and sleepy he turned over, relishing the thought of another two hours at least, but this time his sleep was broken and uneven. He dreamed, a dream that took him away from this peaceful camp and again into conflict, a confused dream of violence and fear.

He woke with a start. It was daylight, though still very early, and he could hear the thud of bare feet running through the camp, and the Thais calling to each other. But it was not that which set his blood pounding and his skin tingling. From the north, distant but quite distinct, came the rattle of a machine-gun and the heavy thunder of bombs.

## 2

# THE SHANS

JASON jumped out of bed, dragged gym shoes on to his bare feet and, still in his pyjamas, ran outside to see Colonel Chula also come bounding out, shaving soap on his cheek, to stare at the forested slopes across the gorge. In the still morning air the sounds of shooting

drifted to them – the crack of rifle shots breaking
through the high ripple of automatic fire, and once
again the sound of bombs. Each explosion was followed by a fractional pause, then the firing swelled up
again fiercer than ever – and then there was one
enormous explosion and the firing dwindled into
scattered single shots. The Akhas stood solemn and
silent as they listened, but the Thai drivers and police
called excitedly, and Jason heard several times the
word 'Tachilek! Tachilek!' in among incomprehensible chatter in Thai. 'What's Tachilek?' he asked.

'A town upstream on the Shan side.' Ignoring the
shaving soap drying on his face Colonel Chula stood
gazing across to the north-west. There were more
excited calls from the Thais, and this time the Akhas
joined in with exclamations and pointing fingers. From
behind a ridge some four to five miles further up the
gorge a column of smoke tinged with the greasy black
of an oil fire rose lazily and hung spreading over the
tree tops.

'Bombing!' Jason was taken aback. 'What are the
Burmese –' He did not finish his question. Colonel
Chula was running towards the camp office and its
telephone.

Quickly Jason dressed and went to the mess, where
he ate a solitary breakfast. Everyone else seemed busy,
and there was no sign of the grim Udom. At last
Colonel Chula appeared, shaved, dressed and pre-
occupied. He was smoking a cheroot very fast, and
frowning, and he spoke to Jason more directly than
usual. 'The Burmese Army has made a surprise move
against the Shans.' At Jason's look of mystification

Chula explained: 'The Shans seek their independence. They do not wish to live under Burmese rule.' He smiled grimly: 'You have, I believe, a similar problem in Britain with the Republican Irish!'

'But how does that affect us here?' Jason looked about. Everything seemed quiet and peaceful.

'Do you notice anything, Jason?'

'No, it all seems quiet.'

'Too quiet. The hill people are slipping away back to their villages. The camp will soon be empty.'

'But why?'

'It is instinct, Jason. They feel safest in their hilltop villages.' He threw away the half-smoked cheroot with an expression of exasperation. 'Just as I had thought we would enjoy a really good Songkran! I fear it means you leaving for our resort at Pattaya at once.'

Jason felt deeply disappointed, but put a brave face on it: 'At least I've seen *some* of your hill country, Colonel!'

Chula grimaced. 'I would have wished you to see more. However . . .' He thought for a moment. 'I have arranged for an aircraft to fly you back, but it will not arrive until two o'clock this afternoon. It would be best for you to go to the Rest House in Ban Phao and wait there. I have, unfortunately, now to go and see what is happening along the border.'

'I'll pack at once.'

'This is very vexatious,' said Colonel Chula, 'but at least we should be able to meet again in Bangkok at the end of your stay. I will arrange for your booking at the Pattaya Palace Hotel to be brought forward.'

Jason ran to pack his suitcase, returned in a few

minutes and swung it up into the waiting jeep. He shook hands, but before climbing in beside the driver said to Colonel Chula: 'I seem to bring you nothing but trouble.'

'*You* do not bring the trouble, Jason – and the last time you helped get us out!' He waved farewell as the driver started up, and called: 'You might just have time to visit Nakhon Wat – but do not be late for the aircraft!'

After the hills the valley seemed hotter than ever and the sun's glare from the baked earth fiercer. The streets of Ban Phao were empty; the shop fronts were open but the market stalls and open-air booths had gone, and of the hill people there was no sign. The jeep turned into the Rest House drive and stopped, and taking his suit-case Jason climbed the steps. This place, too, seemed deserted, but he jerked round at a voice from the shadows: 'So you've got your marching orders too!'

Eyes still dazzled by the glare outside, Jason peered into the dining room and saw the correspondent seated at the long table. 'Oh, hullo.' Jason set down his case and repeated cautiously: 'Marching orders?'

'I got mine half an hour ago – an invitation to return to Bangkok by this afternoon at the latest. With it came a friend to see I complied.' He nodded, and following his glance Jason saw a uniformed policeman of the Border Patrol seated discreetly in a corner.

'Why do you have to leave?'

'In case I see too much.' The journalist smiled. 'I admit to being curious about you, at first – I couldn't see how you were involved; but now I don't believe you are involved at all.'

'Involved in what?' Jason was beginning to feel irritated. What on earth was the man talking about? 'Anyway, why are you being sent away when the trouble's in Burma, across the border?'

'Borders don't mean much in the Triangle, I'm afraid. But we'd better introduce ourselves. My name's Bain, Angus Bain.' He held out his hand and Jason said, 'I'm Jason Wright. But what's this Triangle everyone keeps talking about?'

'The Golden Triangle, my friend – the source of more money and trouble than the Yukon or California gold-fields ever were.'

'But where is it?'

'You're standing in it. The Golden Triangle is the mountain area where Thailand, Laos and Burma meet.'

'But **this** can't be ordinary gold.'

'You're right, it isn't ordinary gold – this is white gold, the most expensive stuff in the world.' He looked again at Jason's doubting expression and leant forward. 'You've looked across into Burma?'

'Yes, of course.'

'Notice any clearings on the hillsides?'

'Yes, many – all over the place.'

'What did you see in them?'

'Well,' Jason spoke defensively. 'It looked like flowers.'

'What flowers were they?'

'I don't know,' said Jason slowly, half to himself.

Certainly that crop had looked unlike anything he had seen cultivated in Borneo, or in the farms of Hong Kong's New Territories. 'I've never seen them before.'

'Those flowers were poppies.'

'Poppies are red,' retorted Jason swiftly. 'These were white – white with a few pink.'

'You're thinking of Flanders poppies, and Armistice Day. These are poppies, all right – and they're the staple crop of every hill village and household up here, and have been for centuries. And from that comes –'

'Opium!' A great light seemed to dawn on Jason. 'Of course!'

'Yes, opium – and from the opium is distilled mor phine and from the morphine is distilled heroin, an that white powder is worth its weight in diamonds, an is the source of more evil than anything else in th world.'

'And you were hoping for a story?'

'I was, but –' the correspondent shrugged again, 'i looks as if I've picked the wrong time. By tomorrow thi border area will be swarming with troops and police and any local drug-runner will be lying very lov indeed.' He sighed: 'I had one particular business I'c have liked to check on, and I had a hunch that thi area might provide some answers.' He sighed again. 'Just my luck, I suppose.'

'By the way,' asked Jason curiously. 'What on earth made you ask if I was involved?'

'Did I say that? I'm sorry.' Bain looked at Jason with his clear grey eyes. 'I just wondered how you came to be up here with Colonel Chula. It's none of my business, of course,' he added carefully.

'Oh, that's simple,' said Jason looking back at him innocently. 'My father knows him – they met in Bangkok. I'm on my way out to Hong Kong for the Easter holidays, and he suggested I have a few days here on the way out. Hong Kong gets a bit boring after a while.'

'Well, this is certainly a change. But here,' Bain looked concerned, 'have you had any breakfast? I'll call the cook!'

'Oh, yes thanks.' Jason laughed. 'One of these enormous Thai breakfasts. I should be all right till tomorrow, at least!'

'They eat well, don't they?' Bain looked at his watch: 'H'm, only just after ten. What time's your aircraft?'

'Two o'clock. But Colonel Chula suggested I might have a look at this Wat place. Would you like to come along?'

'Well, now,' Bain looked at him thoughtfully. 'I wouldn't mind, but I'll have to speak to my watchdog!' To Jason's surprise Bain spoke in Thai. The policeman looked up, his face clouded, then nodded and jumped up.

'He was a bit doubtful till I said that you had been told to go by Colonel Chula.' Bain laughed: 'They certainly hold him in great respect! We'd better take your vehicle – more official!'

One thing had puzzled Jason, and he asked Bain as they bumped along in the jeep: 'How long has this rebellion been going on? Colonel Chula seemed very surprised when he heard the shooting!'

Bain laughed. 'Oh, I think everyone's surprised. The Burmese have left the rebels alone for years because they were anti-communist, though there's a rumour that this might change. But the Shans have been getting money for arms by smuggling drugs, and most of this finds its way to the United States. So the US Government has threatened to cut off all financial aid to the Burmese unless they do something about the drug racket, and it looks as if they've begun.'

The track turned briefly into the forest, but some hundreds of yards in Jason saw a wide clearing ahead littered with the stumps of giant trees and criss-crossed with lines of cinders where the felled trees had been burned away. Around the clearing the tree-tops rose in clumps from a series of small hillocks from fifty to a hundred feet high. Westward rose the long ridge, and north beyond the hillocks Jason saw the same blue mountains of Burma that he had seen from the spur by the forest camp, but from here they seemed closer.

'There's the Laceys' camp.' Bain got out and dusted down his trousers. 'I expect they're out working.'

The driver sat back in his seat and lit a cheroot while Jason, Bain and the policeman escort walked up to the huts and Jason looked round with eager curiosity. Here was no simple jungle camp: these huts, he saw, were strong and carefully made, well thatched with tightly-bound bundles of reed grass – altogether much more solid constructions than the temporary shelters of the forest camp on the ridge. One hut was clearly the Laceys' living quarters, another was a workshop, another a store of some kind, with heavy plank and log frame racks holding a variety of fragments of stone and what looked like pottery, all bearing labels. There were folding tables, camp chairs, a compact generator lighting set in its own hut with cables running out to the others, and electric light bulbs screwed into the heavy rubber at intervals. Jason whistled: this was more of a permanent place than he had thought.

A large thatched garage held two Land Rovers and two empty trailers. All were new, the paint on the body-work gleamed and the tyres were still sharply ridged and black. 'No lack of funds here,' commented Bain. 'Not like some expeditions I've seen.'

A stream flowed past them, disappearing northwards into the trees, and seeing it Jason asked: 'How far's the river?'

'The Kwan gorge? Not much more than a mile, I'd say. But this must be the cookie.'

A plump man in an apron emerged from an open thatched shelter beside the stream. Bain addressed him in Thai and the cook replied, wiping his hands on a large tea-cloth and pointing towards the hillocks.

'They're out working, right enough. We'll walk along.'

It was here very much more open than the forest on the ridge and Jason saw that the smaller bushes had been slashed down and cleared away between the hillocks. He stared, nearly tripping over, and Bain said: 'Watch out, you'll break your ankle if you don't look where you're going.'

'Those things – they're buildings!'

'Of course. What did you think they were?'

'I thought they were small hills!'

'That's what they've looked like for the past thousand years or so. The trees have grown up all over them. Hullo, those must be the Laceys.'

A tarpaulin stretched between two trees sheltered a folding table. Beyond it two figures were busy measuring a large block of stone covered with inscriptions and carvings. One was a tall man, elegant in narrow drill trousers and suede boots, a check shirt open at the neck but carefully buttoned down at the wrists, and with long fair hair combed back over his ears. Beside him worked a smaller figure in scrubbed-pale jeans and blue denim shirt, her fair hair cut short and jammed carelessly under a green canvas hat. At their approach two pairs of polaroid sunglasses swung round at them.

The correspondent spoke first. 'Good morning; my name is Bain and this is Jason Wright. We're visiting Ban Phao and wondered if we might look round?'

'I fear we're rather busy at the moment,' said the tall man. He made no move to shake hands or introduce his companion, but stood with steel tape measure poised, ready to turn back to his work.

At this chilly greeting Jason was about to apologize and turn away when Bain said in his equable voice: 'I see you have found links with Funan.' He pointed to one of the carved bas-reliefs, a formal outline of a six-headed cobra. 'That representation of the *Naga* – isn't that a link with the south?'

Lacey did not turn back to his work. Instead he asked with some surprise: 'What do *you* know of the Empire of Funan?'

Bain gave a faintly apologetic smile. 'Not very much, I'm afraid – and that mainly through gossip. I *do* know that its origin is still a mystery,' he added carefully.

Lacey took off his sunglasses, revealing handsome blue eyes narrowing with interest. 'We think –'

'Peter!' The woman beside him spoke warningly. 'You're forgetting.' She turned to Bain. 'You'll have to excuse us, I'm afraid; our time is very limited, and our labour force has just gone off, leaving us without a word.'

'Of course. I *am* sorry.' Bain smiled apologetically again but still did not go. Jason, embarrassed by his persistence, felt like pulling him away, but the correspondent said to Lacey: 'I'm no archaeologist, but this looks to me as old as Angkor, maybe even older.'

Once again Peter Lacey lowered his steel tape. 'You've been to Angkor recently?'

'Some weeks back. The Khmer Rouge have it now, along with the Viet Cong, but yes – I managed a quick visit before they moved in.'

'Is there much damage?' Lacey, chilly reserve quite vanished, was now all eagerness, ignoring the silent disapproval of the girl beside him. 'I heard that there'd been some fighting round it.'

'Mortaring, mostly; fortunately the US Air Force spared the place. Mortar fire doesn't damage masonry, only people.'

The other heaved a sigh of relief. 'That was always my greatest worry. But you're right about this find; we really think it may be older than Angkor –'

'Which was twelfth century anyway.'

'Much of it, yes. But it's interesting that you should mention Funan; it's always been a mystery. You know its name is a Chinese corruption of the Khmer word "Phnom", meaning mountain?'

'Yes,' Bain nodded.

'We concluded that there *must* have been a capital for a mountain empire, but no one else would admit that such a thing had ever existed.' He spoke with animation, though his colleague, eyes still hidden by her glasses, listened without comment.

'And you think you've found it?'

'I *know* we've found it!' Lacey's eyes gleamed. 'We need more proof, of course, and there are inscriptions on this stele, for instance, which are going to take a bit of deciphering.'

They talked technicalities a moment or two longer, then Bain said: 'I mustn't keep you.'

Lacey, his voice cold again, said: 'I see you have an escort.'

'Oh, that's just officialdom making sure I don't report too much. There's some trouble across in the Shan States.'

'Trouble?'

'Hadn't you heard? Apparently the Burmese Army has moved into the hills against the Shans. That's why your labourers have gone home.'

The Laceys glanced at each other then turned back to their work in silence, and with a jerk of the head Bain signalled to Jason and they moved quietly away.

'They weren't very friendly at first,' said Jason when they were safely past. 'I thought he wasn't going to let us look round at all.'

'They can't stop us,' said Bain. 'It's not their forest. But they're a funny pair, and they were certainly worried about something.'

'Their labour force has pushed off,' Jason reminded him. 'It's bound to hold them up.'

'Yes, I expect that's it.'

Closely followed by the escorting policeman they wandered slowly through the trees. All around were cleared patches where the brush had been slashed down and burnt to reveal some half-overgrown edifice of stone – buildings, rows of huge figures seated in contemplative attitudes, great carved blocks, and one single head, an enigmatic smile on its lips, carved from a rock over thirty feet high. A tangle of ivy growing up round the temples looked like green hair, and the pale mottled lichen growing across the giant cheeks gave it a repulsively leprous appearance. 'This chap could have been the ruler who had this place built,' commented Bain, adding, 'but look at this.' A short way on stood a squat pyramid of stone blocks, the corners wound about by the twisting white roots of giant fig trees, for all the world like cascades of serpents. Above the great doorway was a battle scene, the combatants all monster-headed, while a calm and contemplative figure with features resembling that of the huge carved head gazed down from a padded bolster throne. The stone uprights were carved in the shape of giant snakes, the lintel a pair of snakes interwoven, with hoods upreared. 'The Naga again,' explained Bain. 'These hooded cobras, or hamadryads, represent a half-human, half-serpent race, the Nagas. In Hindu mythology Brahma is said to have ordered them to bite only those who are wholly evil, or those destined to die young. In Buddhism, which took over from the earlier Hinduism, they are often used as door guardians.'

'Someone's been using this place,' called Jason. 'There's quite a well-worn path here.'

'The Laceys, probably.' Bain pushed his way through the undergrowth to look. 'No, it's beaten hard. Perhaps the locals come this way.'

'There's something else,' said Jason. Before the dark doorway were small pegs in the ground and scattered chicken feathers, some new, others brittle and dry. Bain picked one up. 'Domestic,' he said. 'Brown – not the red and black of jungle fowl. There's been some sort of sacrifice here.'

'Who by?'

'Animists. The local hill people probably come down to these old temples to worship the spirits of the woods and the water. Whoever did that,' the journalist pointed to the feathers, 'probably has the snake as his protecting spirit.'

'Have you any matches?' asked Jason, 'It might be worth having a look inside.' He was intrigued by that dark entrance.

'I'd be careful if I were you,' the other warned him. 'There's bound to be all sorts of creepy-crawlies in there, with all the cracks in that stonework where the roots are growing through. Funny smell too – reminds me of something. That escort of ours doesn't like it either,' he added in a low voice, and Jason turned casually to see the policeman standing well back, an expression of unease, almost of fear, on his face. 'Come on, we'll go on down to the river, then it'll be time to start back.'

They walked on down the narrow path, ahead of them the growing rumble of water pouring between steep rock walls. The ground sloped downwards and the air seemed somehow danker. Then Bain stopped.

'There's someone coming.' He stood craning to see through the trees.

'Is it the coolies coming back?'

'No. Quick, turn back.' He swung round and pushed Jason ahead of him and they nearly tripped over the policeman. Bain spoke hastily in Thai, dragging him along by the arm.

'What is it?' Jason had caught the sense of urgency. 'What's wrong?'

'Shans, and they're armed.' He gestured towards the ruins. 'Get behind something.' He pulled at the policeman. 'Come on, man! Don't stop to look.' Reluctantly the policeman followed, and the three of them crouched behind one of the tumbled stone blocks.

Two men walked along the path. Their heads were bound with white kerchiefs covering the hair and knotted at the back, they wore khaki uniform shirts and they held short carbines across the shoulders by the muzzle. They padded along swiftly as if they knew exactly where they were going.

'They'll run into the Laceys!' hissed Jason. 'How can we warn them?'

'I don't think we can. All we can do is let them get ahead and then follow to see what's happened.' They crouched, waiting, and after a minute Bain said: 'Right.' They rose and followed very cautiously along the path, slowing down even more when they came in sight of the clearing – but the Laceys were still there and Bain ran up to them. 'Are you all right?' he asked anxiously. 'A couple of armed men went past us, heading this way.'

'We're all right.' Peter Lacey looked stiff and very tense.

'That's a relief. God knows what they're doing on this side of the river.' He paused looking at Lacey's strained expression. 'Those two men – are they here somewhere?'

'Yes. They're watching us.'

Bain turned round very slowly and Jason followed his gaze. The two Shans stood in the trees, their carbines held casually in the crooks of their arms.

'I'll try them in Thai.' He said a few words, slowly and clearly. There was no response. He repeated them, and one of the Shans smiled slightly and shook his head. 'They don't understand you,' said Lacey. Suddenly Jason had the curious feeling that Peter Lacey was waiting for something else to happen. He seemed to be listening, and his eyes wandered back to the path behind them.

'I don't know what they can want,' said the correspondent, 'but if we try very gently moving off, and looking cheerful and pleasant at the same time, they may just do nothing.' He put on a broad smile, and with a half-salute to the Shans began to walk along the path towards the camp.

'Thakin!' warned one of the Shans, raising his carbine and Bain stopped short. 'That's clear enough.' He looked round at the others. 'I've seen a few stick-ups,' he added, lowering his voice, 'and one thing I've learnt is that the longer you stay the worse you get treated. If we scatter – '

No one replied. Jason looked apprehensively at the two guns covering them. Bain was crazy to suggest making a break for it. In any case, the aircraft would turn up shortly, there'd be no passenger waiting and the

Ban Phao police would come looking for him. And had not Bain himself said that the area would shortly be crawling with police and troops?

'There are only two of them,' Bain went on.

'There are more than two now,' said Lacey.

'Where?'

'Behind you.'

Slowly Bain looked round. Half a dozen Shans, all armed, wearing short-bladed dahs and slung about with bandoleers, haversacks and cartridge belts, were approaching through the trees.

'Look at that fellow!' whispered Jason.

The Shans were led by one of the biggest men he had ever seen – not so much in height as in girth. His khaki shirt strained against a huge chest, and instead of the khaki trousers worn by the others he wore a Burmese lungyi, yard on yard of check cloth wound round him and held at the waist by a great leather belt with a buckle that looked as if it were made from a pound of brass. Under the Shan headcloth the broad face bulged out like a full and golden moon, and as he approached he smiled, his eyes vanishing into the folds of his cheeks like currants in hot dough. He came on swiftly, and still beaming broadly said something to the first two Shans. They replied at once, in rapid speech, and Bain muttered to Jason: 'Something's bothering them.'

The big man, beaming and chuckling and nodding his head and talking half to himself and half to the others, then walked round looking at Bain, then at Jason, and more cursorily at the Laceys. At the Thai policeman he stopped. The man went grey, but the giant spoke to him in Thai, the policeman showed surprised relief and the colour slowly returned to his face.

Then the big Shan stopped his chuckling and smiling, gave a curt order and turned on his heel, walking back in the direction from which he had come.

'That's it, then,' whispered Jason. 'They're going.'

'Don't you believe it,' said the Scot. 'Look at those two.'

The first two Shans beckoned to them to move, to go down the path. Jason reluctant to obey, looked at the two men. 'What do they want?' He looked at the gun muzzles then back at Bain. 'What's happening?'

Bain put it in one succinct sentence: 'We've been kidnapped.'

# 3

# THE VILLAGE

'WHY, why, why?' Jason hurried along the path through the ruins in bewilderment and resentment, but a resentment prudently tempered by caution: the Shans padding along behind, their guns ready, were beginning to look tense and dangerously nervous. Every few yards one would stop and stand facing back towards the clearing and the camp, as if on the look-out for pursuit, and Jason too cast quick glances behind him, hopefully, but the path behind them remained empty, and he thought with frustration of the jeep driver, probably sitting having a cup of tea and chatting with the Laceys' cook, quite unaware that the four Europeans were being marched off by armed men. If only he could get them to fire a shot – then Jason admitted to himself that a shot would hardly be fired except at one of the prisoners. Gritting his teeth and controlling the temptation to make a run for it, he kept up the hurried pace.

They passed the squat, snake-carved pyramid with its root-bound walls and abruptly the ruins ended, the last of the tumbled stonework and creeper-grown monuments giving way to the final slope down to the river. The roar of water grew louder as they hurried down, the air damper and the vegetation yet more lush, and for the last few yards of their approach to the gorge the dark green leaves of the forest palms glistened with moisture. Ahead Jason saw daylight, shafts of sunlight striking down through the trees, and there before them was the gorge, forty yards wide and with rock walls against which greeny-white water surged and pounded. It looked quite impassable at first, till he saw the tops of great boulders set like giant stepping stones at the mouth of a longer, deeper stretch. There, on the bank, the Shans halted them.

It was warm in the gorge, warm and damp and noisy, and the upflung spray settled in a fine, soaking mist on their clothes and hair, but Jason ignored it, his eyes and mind busy. The water looked too dangerous to try, but if he could *now* make a bolt for the trees he might get away – then his eyes rested once more on those casually held weapons, in particular on the two shotguns. They were automatic shotguns, he could see from their length of smooth steel breech, and, he guessed, were probably loaded with buckshot. The thought sent a quick shiver down his spine. It was no good.

There was a word or two and then the big Shan led the Thai policeman aside, speaking to him in a low voice while Bain strained unsuccessfully to overhear. The Shan finished by resting his huge hand on the policeman's shoulder and giving him an encouraging clap, and the young man, with a final nod of understanding, gave a last look round and set off at a quick walk back along the path.

'He's taken the message, whatever it is,' muttered Bain. In a low voice he asked Peter Lacey: 'Have you any idea what this is all for?'

Lacey shrugged. 'None at all.'

'I'll bet it's something to do with the fighting – watch out,' he added hastily, 'they're signalling, and that fat fellow means business.'

Down, waved the Shans, go down, and the prisoners slithered down till they were standing right at the water's edge. The big Shan already stood on the first boulder, and Jason grinned nervously to himself, visualizing that huge bulk slipping and falling in, raising fountains of water and sending yet higher waves washing out against the rock walls – but with surprising agility the Shan sprang from boulder to boulder and, safe on the far side, turned and waved them across.

'I'll go.' Bain climbed up on to the first boulder and set off, springing easily from one to another while Jason watched.

Jason hesitated. 'Thakin!' warned a Shan behind him and he scrambled unwillingly up to the first boulder and began his journey across. He paused a moment between each jump, wondering if he could somehow vanish into the green depths of that long pool beyond – then saw the big man on the far bank watching him, head cocked to one side and carbine ready. Still pausing deliberately between each short spring, as if he was merely being extra careful not to fall in and had never for a moment entertained any thought of escape, Jason finished the crossing and sprang down beside Bain. Still beaming, but with his little eyes sharp with suspicion, the big Shan gave Jason a close stare before turning to watch the others.

A group of Shans then crossed, followed by the Laceys, and finally the last two Shans jumped down beside them. There was a chuckle from the big man, and an arm like a buffalo's foreleg waved them on and up.

'Might as well get on with it.' Bain set off up the steep path and Jason followed. 'That policeman will be in Ban Phao soon,' he said hopefully. 'Colonel Chula's bound to send out a rescue party.'

'A posse?' Bain smiled grimly but did not pause in his steady climb up the path – here so steep that in some stretches they helped themselves up with their hands. 'Not much use to us, I fear.'

'Why not?' Jason paused to avoid the stones and dust trickling back from Bain's heels. 'He's got enough men.'

'He couldn't help us if he had an army.' Bain climbed on steadily. 'Don't you realize where we are?'

Jason stopped short, but scrambled on again as from behind Lacey bumped into him. 'Sorry,' he said mechanically, then ahead to Bain: 'D'you mean – '

'Yes,' said Bain, again without looking round. 'We're in Burma, and we're in rebel territory as well. There's not a thing Colonel Chula can do.'

They climbed steadily, with frequent halts for rest, and there was little talk though occasionally Jason heard a brief muttered conversation between the Laceys. The Shans gave them water from large, military-style water-bottles, and Jason was thankful that their captors, whatever their motives, seemed personally well enough disposed towards them. In two hours they reached an abandoned village on the shoulder of the hill, no more than half a dozen half-collapsed thatched houses set among terraced fields, the thin earth overgrown with weeds. Here they sat for a longer rest, leaning against the thatch of a collapsed roof.

'The fields are worked out.' Bain wiped the sweat from his eyebrows. 'The soil's poor anyway, and when it's been worked down to dust the area's abandoned and the village moves.' He cocked an eye at Jason: 'How are you managing?'

'I'm all right.' He was soaked with sweat, but already he could feel the hill breeze distinctly chilly. 'Lucky I had my jersey with me.' He had tied it round his waist by the arms while he climbed; once he dried a bit he'd put it on. Then he looked at the correspondent, dressed

for the warmth of the Ban Phao valley, and Bain caught
his glance: 'I wish I'd been given a little notice of this
tour. The Laceys don't seem too well off either. At
least she's got her shoulder-bag!'

'Listen!' In the clear air they heard the faint hum of
an aircraft engine.

'More bombing?' hazarded Bain. 'Where's it
coming from?'

'It's coming from back there!' Jason flung out an
arm, pointing out over the gorge far below, 'from the
Ban Phao strip!' He thumped his knee in vexation. 'It's
two o'clock! That's the aircraft sent to collect me!' At
his outburst the Laceys looked round, but before Jason
could explain his anguished cry the Shans called:
'Thakin!' and motioned to them to get up and walk on.
Jason thought he caught sight of a speck in the
southern sky, but quickly lost it. He walked on again,
his heart heavy.

The abandoned village marked the summit of the
steepest part of the hill rising from the gorge. Running
back from it, though always climbing, the ridge rose
more evenly, with easier walking through the thin
forest, through open patches where the jungle had been
slashed down, burnt, cultivated and again abandoned,
and over stretches where open rock showed through.
They walked steadily, again with frequent halts for
rest, but with little conversation. The Laceys seemed
glumly resigned to their capture, and Bain and Jason
were each busy with their own thoughts.

At one halt, however, the two archaeologists interrupted their own low talk to quiz their new companions. After identifying Bain as a journalist, the

woman turned curiously to Jason. 'Will you tell me
your name again?'

'Wright – Jason Wright.'

'I *thought* I'd heard Jason!' Her face showed some
animation. 'Do you remember, Peter, when we thought
we'd identified traces of that old pirate on the Black Sea
coast? We were working on a site in Turkey,' she
explained to Jason, 'and I'd always been interested in
the Argonaut story – founded on fact, of course.'

'We found nothing,' interrupted Peter Lacey
brusquely. 'Now I wonder where that big fellow's
taking us?'

'It's rather worrying,' she said apologetically, 'Peter's
not very well – he has to have injections.'

'Never mind that now, Meg.' He spoke curtly, and
she fell silent again. It was clear that they were not
disposed to conversation, and Jason turned to Bain.
'Fatso there' – he nodded to the big man – 'I thought
he'd hardly be able to climb on a bus, but he's setting
quite a pace!'

'Fatso!' Bain gave a wry smile. 'I hope he doesn't
speak English!' They talked in desultory fashion till
they were ordered to set off again.

The afternoon shadows were lengthening when they
reached the village, coming on it suddenly where the
ridge levelled out briefly before rising to a crest, with
beyond it a background of yet higher crests and peaks.
From a short distance the houses looked all jumbled
together at all sorts of odd angles, but as they approached Jason saw that each was set on its own terrace,
and that a horse-shoe-shaped open space had been left
clear at the nearer end. Jason felt that they were under

scrutiny as they approached between the sickle-shaped terraced patches of poppy cultivation, and sure enough armed men ran out to greet them as they passed under a large arch of dressed tree-trunks leading to the open space. These men were Shans, but the women husking rice by the houses he recognized by their black clothing and head-dresses of silver coins to be Akhas. Had any of them been across at the forest camp? He looked round, trying to see from their expressions whether they recognized him – but he had little time to specu-late, for as they reached the first houses they were halted.

'Looks as if we're here for the night, at least,' whispered Bain. 'Can't say I'm sorry to stop!'

Then the Laceys were led away by one of the Shans, disappearing through the houses at the top, slightly higher end of the village, and for a while there was a discussion among the Shans, with the fat man, all smiles but with his eyebrows well up, talking and arguing with several others. 'I'll tell you what it is,' said Bain in a whisper out of the side of his mouth. 'They were all prepared for the Laceys – but we're an unexpected bonus, and they've got nowhere to keep us!'

At last there was some sort of agreement, though the fat man shook his head with angry chuckles, and the two prisoners were led to a small building set near the entrance to the open space. It was unlike the other houses, which were set up on piles and had verandahs and open bamboo-work beneath the thatch. This was a small, strong building, windowless, and set on the ground. 'Looks like the village store!' commented

Bain. 'Strong little place. Brrrr – it's chilly!' He
stamped his feet, and Jason too felt the chill as the
warmth of the day's walking ebbed away and the sweat
dried on him. He felt reluctant to put on his jersey
when the other had nothing, but Bain said, 'No sense in
two of us catching cold,' and Jason pulled it on over
his head. That *had* been a stroke of luck: if he hadn't
been too lazy to untie the sleeves it would now be
sitting in the jeep.

'At least we'll be warmer in here,' said the correspondent. 'Aha – they're going to have it opened up.'

The heavy plank door was secured by a thick beam
set tightly in wooden sockets. A Shan beckoned, one of
the Akha men ran up and drove the beam out with
blows from a heavy, mallet-like club, the door swung
open and they were motioned inside.

Bain sniffed: 'A bit unventilated?'

Behind them the heavy door was pulled to and the
beam driven tight into its socket again with heavy
thwacks from the mallet. Jason winced: 'Noisy thing,
that.'

'One of the best locks ever invented,' commented
the Scot. 'Whenever that door is opened the whole
village knows about it. Now let's just see what we've
got here.'

The close-fitting planks and the heavy roof of thatch
shut out most of the daylight, but enough filtered
through the gaps between wall and thatch to allow
them to move about cautiously, while gradually their
eyes became used to the weak light.

Jason began feeling his way round the walls, running
his fingers over the rough surfaces – gently, for fear of

splinters – then his hand met something which felt like a lighter version of the plank door to the outside. 'Here's something!' He ran his hands up and down: 'It's like a wide cupboard set against the end here.' Further on he met a familiar shape and called: 'A lock! They've got a big padlock on this thing!' He tugged, but it did not budge. 'It's strong. What d'you think they keep here?'

'Their opium, of course.' Bain was quietly scraping with his penknife at the junction of two vertical wall planks. 'The first thing to do's to see out.' He worked away quietly, occasionally pausing to puff away the powdery scrapings, and Jason saw a lengthening thread of daylight show between the planks. 'See anything?'

Bain signalled for silence, put down his penknife and set an eye to the crack, then sat back and said in a low voice: 'I thought we might get out through the thatch,' and he jerked a thumb upwards, 'but I'm afraid we wouldn't get very far.'

'Why not?'

'There's a sentry outside with one of their fancy shot-guns, and a good half-dozen more Shans lounging about further on.'

'Perhaps we could try after dark!'

'We'd have to see a bit more first. We'll make one or two more of these observation slits,' and he set to work again with his penknife. Eventually there were a little series of small peep-holes; by moving from one to another they were able to see pretty well what went on among the village houses around.

'Not too much going on,' said Bain after a long series of looks out, and Jason reluctantly agreed with him.

Around them the houses on their stilts were unoccupied
except for a child or two on the open, bamboo-fenced
verandahs, with occasionally a woman appearing,
rinsing out a pot and throwing the water out into the
dusty compound below. Under the houses the domestic
animals rootled – a small black pig, two or three dogs
with pointed snouts and short hair, and once from the
shadows the head of a pony. Against their hut wall
sprawled their sentry, shotgun across his knees. He was
smoking, and from inside Jason caught whiffs of his
cigar. Bain wrinkled his nose: 'The cheapest – chopped
tobacco stalk wrapped in corn-cob leaf.'

'Do you smoke?' asked Jason.

'No.' Bain gave a brief shake of the head.

'It's getting on.' Peering out they saw the day's
activities drawing to a close. There now seemed to be
more people about, with black-clothed Akhas, mainly
women, returning from the fields. They carried with
them small earthenware pots, packed into baskets and
heavy, rather clumsy-looking curved knives which
reminded Jason of miniature billhooks.

'Someone's coming!' They jumped back from their
observation slits. Again came the reverberating thuds
of the beam being hammered open, the door swung
back and there were two Shans, both armed but with
their weapons slung, and an Akha woman, holding a
pair of enamel plates as big as small basins, heaped with
rice, vegetables and chopped pork. She giggled with
embarrassment, turning her head away from the two
prisoners as she proffered the bowls.

'That's more like it!' Bain took one of the bowls and
said something in Thai – to which the woman only

replied with another embarrassed laugh. 'Come on, Jason, take yours.' As soon as Jason had taken his plate the woman turned and ran, her giggles trailing behind her. They were about to re-enter their prison when one Shan stopped them and the other brought up two round, wicker-work stools, and themselves went off a few yards to sit and smoke and chat in low voices while the prisoners ate.

Jason quickly realized that he had not eaten since breakfast. What had appeared an enormous plateful of rice soon vanished, and when his plate was empty one of the Shans came up with a cup of water. 'They mean to keep us alive, at least!' Bain put down his plate with a sigh of satisfaction. 'Nothing like a bit of food to raise one's morale! I think I might even try one of their cigars.' He gestured, holding fingers to his lips in the attitude of smoking and a Shan rummaged in his ornamented cloth shoulder-bag and produced a fat white cheroot though shaking his head disparagingly. 'He means it's not much good, Jason – but I'll try it anyway.' Bain took it and the Shan brought up a glowing ember from the fire. Bain puffed hard and managed to keep it alight, though he coughed and choked, and tears came to his eyes. The Shan laughed in sympathy.

Blinking and rubbing his eyes Bain then indicated that they could do with a stroll round. After a shouted consultation with someone invisible among the houses this man nodded, and the two prisoners were escorted through the ceremonial gateway at the end of the cleared space, to sit looking out over the edge of the ridge. Jason stared south towards Thailand, at the long ridge which stood like a black barrier against the westering sun. Somewhere in that stretch of forested mountain was Colonel Chula, their one outside hope of rescue. Jason shivered suddenly, and said hastily to Bain: 'Getting pretty cold, isn't it?'

But the correspondent was staring out over the blue ridges to the west. 'Listen!' He gestured for silence.

Then Jason heard it too – the faintest irregular crepitation, rather like the sound of Chinese firecrackers in the distance. The sounds, at first intermittent, grew and swelled in volume, then dwindled and died away, with only the occasional distant crack to break the silence.

'Somebody's won,' remarked Bain. At Jason's look he explained: 'When you hear small-arms fire suddenly swell up, it means only one thing – an infantry attack. It's either successful, or it's not – and in either case there's not much more shooting. The trouble is,' he went on thoughtfully, 'we don't know *which* lot won.'

'Perhaps it was the Burmese Army,' said Jason hopefully.

'You mean they'll then be able to come along and rescue us?' Bain grimaced. 'Being liberated isn't always pleasant! Anyhow, we'll know one way or another soon.'

Their guards had also heard the firing and were staring at the ridges west of them and talking excitedly, while other Shans came running out from among the houses to listen.

'They don't know who's winning either,' said the journalist with a certain satisfaction, adding resignedly, 'and that makes us' – he sighed – 'even more valuable hostages.'

'Thakin!' called the guards.

'Back we go,' and they walked slowly up through the arch and into the clearing. 'No sign of the Laceys – perhaps they're having their constitutional on the far side.' He looked into the hut. 'Aha, they're doing us proud.' Inside were two woven mats, and on each a bright red blanket, striped with black at the ends. 'We'll be pretty snug in here.' The Shans were about to swing the door to when Bain pointed to his cheroot, which was quite out, and made the sign of striking a match. The Shan fumbled in his bag and drew out a box and was about to strike one when Bain, with an easy, assured smile made the motions of relighting the cigar again and again, pocketed the box, waved his thanks and went inside and sat on his blanket. The Shan hesitated, shrugged, then swung the door to and again the prisoners felt the hut reverberate as the beam was hammered home.

Jason watched the pantomime with bafflement. 'What was all that about?' he asked. 'I thought you didn't smoke!'

'I don't.' The correspondent ground out the cheroot with a small shower of sparks. 'But it got us some matches.' He pointed up to the thatch. 'If everything else fails we may have to burn our way out.'

'Tonight?' Jason felt his heart sink. He was infinitely weary, the hot food after the long hours of toil up the ridge had left him suddenly comatose, and the thick red blanket on the mat looked infinitely inviting. To his relief Bain said: 'No, not tonight. First, we must get some rest — otherwise we wouldn't get very far before being picked up again. Second — we may be exchanged tomorrow; for all we know negotiations may be going on at this very moment. But the most important thing,' he said, 'is that we might get badly burnt ourselves. No.' He shook his head decisively, and Jason could just see his eyes gleam in the growing dark. 'Fire is our last resort. Now, we'd better sleep while we can.' He spread out the mat and unrolled the blanket on it. 'At least there are no mosquitoes at this height. Goodnight, Jason.'

'Goodnight.' Jason too spread out the mat, unrolled the red blanket and lay down and wrapped himself in it. His eyes closed almost before his head fell back.

Jason slept heavily till the early morning cold woke him. It was still dark, and he rolled himself tighter in his blanket and tried to sleep again, but as with the morning before his sleep was interrupted by violent dreams. In this one he was staring up at a tiny flame in a corner of the thatch. It licked up higher, drifts of smoke coiled down into their prison but he and Bain could not open the door. The flame grew fiercer, then the whole roof caught and sparks were blown on to the Akha houses across the open space. Flames leapt skywards, children screamed and ponies strained to break loose ... The fire spread from roof to roof, flames leapt up and the night clouds turned red ... He groaned and tossed, though someone was trying to get him out, someone who called him by name: 'Jason! Jason!' He struggled but the voice called insistently: 'Jason!' and he opened his eyes.

The morning light glowed red through a fold of the blanket lying over his face. He pulled it aside, and there was Bain, looking down at him in concern. 'You were shouting about fire! You must have been having a nightmare! Are you all right?'

Jason sat up, rubbing his face. It had seemed horribly real, and he looked around, still expecting to see smoke and to hear the roar and crackle of flames – but all was quiet. 'I am all right, thanks.' He took a deep breath. 'Sorry I woke you.'

'I've been awake for some time,' said Bain. 'It got pretty cold about four in the morning.' He rubbed his bristly chin. 'Unfortunately my razor's at that Rest House, with the remainder of my gear. M'm,' he wrapped the blanket round him while he sat on the floor. 'I could do with a cup of tea.' He looked at his watch. 'Six thirty; I wonder if it's too early for room service?'

Jason attempted a smile and wrapping his own blanket around him, stumbled across to the nearest observation slit. At first he could see little, but as the light strengthened there was more movement. Shrouded figures hurried between the houses, a dog wandered out and scratched itself in the dust, a cock crew, the small black pigs under the houses snuffled and grunted and, louder than everything else, came the morning coughs of the cheroot smokers, the hawkings and the expectorations. 'The Song of Asia,' said Bain with a grimace. The village was awakening.

From outside their hut came closer coughs, the scratch of a match and the acrid whiff of a cheroot, and the fiercer cough as their sentry took his first puffs of the day. 'I'll see if he can get us something,' said Bain. He hammered on the door and called: 'Chiyah! Chay! Tsaah!' and, finally 'Tea!' in a loud voice, then peered through one of the cracks, explaining to Jason: 'I don't speak any Burmese, but that was tea in half a dozen other languages.' He peered through again, and said: 'I think it's going to work! He's heading off towards one of the houses, he's having a word with someone, he's coming back –' Jason waited impatiently, and finally Bain called: 'Here we are!'

The same Akha woman who had brought their meal of rice the evening before appeared, the beam was hammered out and the door swung open. The woman was still dressed in her finery, the helmet of silver coins still decorated her hair ('Does she sleep in it?' wondered Jason) but there were also the signs of this morning's work – a smudge of charcoal on one cheek and ash speckling her black leggings. She saw the glances and with another giggle put down a large black kettle, three metal bowls and ran off.

'Come on,' Bain said to the Shan. 'Let's try the tea.' The Shan grinned and poured out three bowls, then brought up the wickerwork stools again, and they sat outside companionably as they sipped the hot brew. It was without milk or sugar, and reminded Jason of the slightly scented tea given after meals in Chinese restaurants, and Bain confirmed his guess. 'It's Chinese tea, all right, probably grown locally by the Haus.'

'The *who*?' Jason blinked. There seemed to be more and more of these unfamiliar tribes up here.

'The Haus – descendants of Chinese immigrants who married local people, and who maintain many of their old Chinese ways. They're not too popular, being more warlike than most of the other hill peoples.'

'Well, they don't grow a bad blend of tea!' Jason then looked up towards the clustering houses higher up. 'No sign of the Laceys!'

Bain smiled rather sardonically. 'They're in the more exclusive quarter! I expect we're being kept apart quite deliberately, in case we all try to escape.' He shook his head, repeating half to himself: 'They're a funny pair.'

'The woman's not exactly polite!'

Bain shot him a surprised glance. 'What makes you say that?'

'Well –' Jason hesitated. 'She was pretty rude about my name.'

'Was she?' Bain frowned, then laughed. '*I* remember! She said that your namesake was an old pirate. Was that it?'

Jason grinned rather shamefacedly. 'That was it.'

'You should be flattered that she knew. So he was.'

'A pirate?' Jason stared. 'He was an Argonaut!'

'The Argonauts were pirates, all right. What do you think they were doing, roaming the Black Sea?'

'But the Golden Fleece,' expostulated Jason. 'Surely that was a symbolic quest?'

'Rubbish, boy, there was nothing symbolic about it. They weren't after the fleece, they were after the gold.' At Jason's puzzled face Bain patiently explained. 'In the Caucasus gold was panned from the stream-beds by washing the gold-bearing sand over a sheep's fleece nailed to a board. The heavy grains of gold were trapped in the wool and the lighter sand was washed away. No, Jason, your high-minded Argonauts were a bunch of adventurers after the gold stores of Kolkhida, at the east end of the Black Sea.' He gave an ironic smile. 'It must have sounded fine and romantic to talk about the quest for the Golden Fleece, but they themselves knew just what they were after. So,' added Bain, 'Miss Lacey was right. Satisfied?'

'Well –' Jason didn't know whether to feel aggrieved at this stark and coldly probable explanation for the old legend – or to feel secretly pleased that his namesake had not only actually existed but had been a bit of a desperado to boot.

'Anyway,' Bain put down his cup. 'We've got our own bunch of adventurers to think about.'

Around them the village was busy, and the women were streaming down to the terraced fields just over the edge of the ridge. 'No Shan women here?' asked Jason.

'The Shans are valley people – this bunch probably have their families down in the valley just west of here.'

'If they're valley people, what are they doing up here?'

'They claim the hills between as well, and, of course, the opium from the poppies grown on them – which provides the funds for arms with which to fight the Burmese.'

'But what on earth can they want with us?'

Bain shook his head slowly. 'I've been racking my brains on that one since yesterday – and I can't find an answer.'

Just then their morning rice arrived and their discussion was interrupted while they dealt with it and were then taken for a short stroll under the eyes of the two guards. They were then led back to their hut and locked in. For a while they talked in desultory fashion, discussing the demands the Shans might be making for their release, the chances of the Burmese Army reaching them, even the chances of escaping – though this possibility seemed remote. One thing, however, had been nagging Jason's mind, and as the talk flagged he was able to lie back on his blanket and think till eventually he turned to Bain, also stretched out on his blanket, and said rather apologetically: 'You know you told me about coming up here on a hunch, and that it had something to do with the Burmese attack.'

'Yes. I did.' Bain leant up on one elbow, studying him.

'It couldn't have been for that, could it? I mean, you must have known that if there was trouble you'd be sent back to Bangkok. So I think – ' here Jason spoke rather awkwardly, 'I think that you originally came up here to find something quite different.'

For a moment or two Bain did not reply. He tapped his fingers on the earth floor, still looking closely at Jason then, as if satisfied, sank back on to his blanket. 'Yes,' he said, staring up at the thatch. 'You are right. I came up to find something quite different. I'd better tell you about it.'

# 4
## FIRE

JASON settled himself comfortably on his red blanket and Bain, reflectively and rather slowly, said: 'For centuries these hills have produced opium. With their poor soil there wasn't much else that would grow except the poppy, and steady but comparatively small quantities of opium were produced, both for the opium dens of the East and as a pain-killer. Then the Vietnam war began, and the US troops in South Vietnam offered a new, very large market for drugs – and at the same time the traditional major suppliers of narcotic drugs for America, Turkey, clamped down on opium growing under US Government pressure. The drug racketeers, therefore, turned their attention here. With their encouragement these hills became the world's single biggest opium-producing area, and because of the money this made was christened the Golden Triangle. Are you with me so far?'

'Yes.' Jason nodded.

'In the old happy days of easy smuggling along the Mediterranean, it was not difficult to ship the raw opium to chemical factories in places like Marseilles, where it could be distilled first into morphine and then into heroin for shipment to the pushers in the United States. But here it was different. Opium is bulky, and with the greater distances and poor communications this bulk became an important factor.'

'Go on,' said Jason. 'That's quite straightforward.'

'The first step in distilling opium – turning it into morphine – is comparatively simple – it's just a matter of making repeated "brews" and extracting the condensate with lime. The basic equipment is a couple of old oil drums and a straining cloth. So the opium lords began to distil their own morphine *before* exporting their goods. Understood?'

Jason nodded again; this was all clear enough.

'But there is another advantage to making your own morphine besides overcoming the bulk factor: it fetches, wholesale, about eight times as much as the opium. The opium lords set up numbers of small refineries very close to the actual growing areas, and soon a stream of morphine was pouring out of the Triangle – to the GIs in South Vietnam and to the international racketeers. These last, of course, arranged for their newly-purchased morphine to be further distilled into heroin, not because of any bulk factor, simply because of the huge profit they made. Heroin is a much more potent drug – and it fetches five times as much as morphine, wholesale.'

'Whew!' Jason whistled softly. 'So by the time the stuff's been turned into heroin it's –' he paused, then said with surprise: 'forty times the price of opium. Is that really true?'

'Oh, yes, and remember, that's wholesale. With retail the ratios are very much greater. Now all this was not unknown to the opium lords. They would have dearly loved to distil their own heroin on the spot and get the enormously inflated price themselves. But turning morphine into heroin is a very much more delicate and complicated business than getting morphine from opium. The morphine has to be bonded with acetic acid, undergoing a complicated five-stage process. It needs some quite advanced equipment and, above all, trained chemists.'

'M'm, yes.' Jason grimaced. 'I can see they'd have liked to make their own, but –'

'Exactly: the Triangle is a pretty primitive area, and not a very safe one for an establishment of that nature, with all these odd warring groups about. So for a long time it was felt that the opium lords would never be able to produce their own heroin. Some locally-produced heroin actually did begin to appear, but the United Nations Narcotics Bureau found that it was being made in factories in Thailand itself, and with the Thai police they were able to do something about it. In any case it was inferior stuff, what is called Grade Three, which is only three to six per cent pure and therefore fetches a low price.'

'And then?'

'Quite right, Jason. Suddenly, heroin of almost complete purity began to appear in Bangkok, Saigon and Vientiane. It was Grade Four, which is up to ninety-nine per cent pure. It fetched top prices – and no one has been able to find out where it is coming from! It's a fluffy white powder, and it comes in plastic bags holding about seven-eighths of a kilo – say about two pounds. These bags carry quite distinctive trademarks printed on them in blue. One is a coiled-up dragon, another is a globe with a tiger springing across it.' He smiled. 'If ever you come across any plastic bags of that nature, full or empty, I'd be glad to hear!'

'And you came up to Ban Phao looking for the factory?'

'No, not for the factory. I reckoned it was inside the Shan States – and I didn't expect to get in! Nor was I going to look about on the Thai side; the United Nations narcotics agents as well as the Thai police are active there, and would find out more than I ever could.'

'I met a United Nations chap in Ban Phao,' broke in Jason. 'He said he was to do with education – but I think he wanted to have a good look at me before I went up to the border.'

'Education is a good cover for a Narcotics Bureau man.' Bain was clearly interested. 'How did he know you were going up there?'

'Oh, he was actually Colonel Chula's cousin, or half-cousin, or something like that. His name was Varalak.'

'Oh, Varalak!' Bain laughed. 'You don't want to worry about *him* being an agent! He's a well-known socialite. No,' and he laughed again. 'I can't see Varalak hunting down crooks!'

'You know him then?'

'Anyone who's been to any big function in Bangkok will have met Varalak! And I gather he's well-known to the New York hostesses, too!'

'Oh.' Jason was secretly rather disappointed. He had visualized the suave, dapper Varalak as something more than a wealthy man about town. 'I'm sorry,' he apologized, 'I interrupted. You were telling me what you were looking for.'

'Oh, yes,' Bain went on. 'Wherever the factory may be, heroin is getting through, and I think it's getting through at Ban Phao. If it is, someone is *letting* it through, otherwise something would have been discovered by now. What I want to find out, Jason, is who is getting it through the border patrols and check points – quite a difficult business. Once we identify him the heroin route will reveal itself.'

Jason sat hugging his knees, quite engrossed. It was all a bit far-fetched, of course – but intriguing for all that. Entering into the spirit of the puzzle he asked: 'Have you any clues as to who this chap might be?'

Angus Bain smiled faintly. 'I call him Mr Snow,

after the colour of the stuff he deals in. Yes,' he said in answer to Jason's question. 'I think I do have a few ideas though they're pretty general ones, I'm afraid. I'll try them out on you.'

'Go on.'

'Right, we'll begin,' said Bain. 'First question: who has dealings with border patrols and check points – an official or a business man?'

'An official.'

'Next question: would he be a man of lesser or greater authority?'

'Greater, probably.'

'Third question: where would such an official be based – here, or Bangkok?'

'If he were of greater authority it would be Bangkok.'

'If he were based in Bangkok how would he be able to find out about patrols and checks up here, in this remote area?'

'He would have to be connected with the area in some way – perhaps in charge of some department concerned with the area.'

'Would this man be poor or would he be wealthy?'

'If he is dealing in heroin he is probably wealthy – though he may not show it,' added Jason swiftly.

'Agreed. Now, let us see what we have deduced. Mr Snow is a Government official of considerable authority, probably based in Bangkok, in a department dealing with this area and also wealthy – though possibly unostentatiously.' Bain paused, and said, very gently: 'Do you know anyone who fits all those requirements, Jason?'

'There must be dozens and dozens of officials who

fit,' said Jason with a shock of anger. 'Why ask me?' He saw the understanding look in Bain's eyes and apologized awkwardly: 'I'm sorry, I didn't mean to be rude, I was just a bit surprised –'

'Forget it,' said Bain. 'That's all right.' He lay back again, reflective once more. 'I'm determined to expose this link in this vicious drug racket. I've seen youngsters like yourself hooked and destroyed by it, and all for money.' Then he sighed. 'Heaven knows how I'm going to find out anything locked up in here.'

For some time Jason lay thinking. He knew that drugs brought racketeers enormous profits – yet he found it difficult to connect this remote mountain area, with its poverty-stricken villagers and neglected air, with the international smuggling gangs that caused so much misery in Europe and the States. And journalists were always on the look-out for stories of some kind!

The morning dragged past. At intervals the two prisoners rose to pace their little prison like caged tigers, again and again speculating on what the terms for their exchange might be. At length Bain said: 'There's something I haven't mentioned as yet, in case I depressed you, but I think you'd better know. The Shan rebels already have two other European hostages. They've had them a couple of months already, and it doesn't look as if they're going to let them go till they get what they want.'

Jason turned on him a face of dismay. 'I've heard nothing of this!'

'You wouldn't, because these men were snatched in Burma itself. They are two Russian doctors – Boris Pyanitskiy and Stanislav Vinogradov.'

'What are they being held for?'

'There's a Shan leader called Hkunsa in jail in Rangoon. The Burmese, however, have so far refused to give him up, so the Shans have simply held on to the two doctors.'

'Whereabouts are they – have you any idea?'

'Not the remotest – though it's likely to be up near Kengtung.'

'I see,' said Jason slowly. 'You're in fact telling me that we might be held here for some time.'

'A lot depends on how the Burmese Army gets on, but their operation may simply be to close the border. It would take them much time and many men to subdue the whole of the Shan States – if, indeed, they could.'

Jason was silent for a short while, then said: 'In that case we'd better try and get out.'

'I think so too.' Bain got up. 'We'll just examine these walls once more.'

They very quickly found that their earlier suspicions had been correct: the plank walls were too strong to be breached without proper tools and considerable noise. 'No,' said Bain in his precise voice, rather as if he were expressing the only possible conclusion to a geometrical theorem, 'It must be the roof.'

'You mean burn our way out?' Jason looked soberly up at the thick roof of thatch above their heads, and another thought struck him: 'That stuff in their store, the opium.'

'That'll go up too, Jason, just like resin. But I don't intend us simply to burn our way out.' Bain was walking about, trying to examine the construction of the roof.

'What I think we might do is prepare a hole on the rear side of the roof thatch, and when we're ready to go, set light to the front.'

'So while the Shans are running for the door –'

'– we slip out the back way and bolt for the trees. What do you think?'

'That's more like it!' Jason drew a secret breath of relief. Not only did the plan sound feasible, but there would be less risk from the fire.

Bain looked up at the roof and then at Jason. 'I'm still a bit heavier than you are,' he said. 'You get up on my shoulders and have a look at the thatch. See how thick it is and whether you think anything can be done.'

'Right. I'll take off my shoes.'

'M'm – good idea!' Bain gave an appreciative grimace, crouched against one of the stout corner posts, head down and shoulders hunched, and put his clasped hands behind him. 'Manage?'

'Okay.' Jason put his stockinged foot into the stirrup of the correspondent's hands and pushed himself up on to his shoulders, steadying himself with one hand on the plank walls. He moved carefully, anxious not to slip against the wood and alert the guard outside to what was going on. Very cautiously he straightened up and, still steadying himself with one hand, with the other explored the thatch, now close to his face. He ran his hands over a portion of it, and then tried pushing his fingers through. Though it was closely packed he found that by pushing his open hand through to the wrist he at last met outside air. He withdrew his hands, and prodded about, gently, but apart from the framework of

split bamboo on to which the thatch was lashed in tight
overlapping bundles, there seemed to be no other
obstruction. Below him Bain, still crouched against the
corner post, said nothing, but when Jason bent, put a
hand on his shoulder and sprang lightly to the ground
the correspondent straightened up with a grunt of
relief. He rolled his eye at Jason as he rubbed his
shoulders: 'I'm beginning to think I was wrong about
your weight! You're pretty solid! Where d'you get all
that bulk from?'

'Well,' Jason grinned, self-consciously. 'I do a bit of
swimming!'

For a moment a faint flicker of recognition appeared
in the journalist's eyes, his brow furrowed momentarily,
then cleared as he gave a slight shake of the head:
'Well, whatever it is, it puts beef on you! Anyway, what
did you find?'

'The thatch won't stop us. It's only a hand's breadth
thick and the framework bamboos are a good twelve to
fourteen inches apart. We'll get through.'

'That's just fine! Once we're into the trees . . .'
They talked in eager whispers, the frustration and bore-
dom of the last twenty-four hours falling away.

'There's one thing.' Jason's face fell suddenly. 'The
Laceys! We can't just go off and leave them. And he's
sick.'

'I did think of them,' said Bain, 'and it struck me
that if we did get away they'd have a better chance of
being exchanged. First, it would give the Burmese some
idea of where they were and exactly who had them –
for there are several independent Shan groups. As for
Peter Lacey, perhaps the Burmese Air Force would

drop some insulin for him – the Shans are decent
enough, they'd see he got it.'

'I suppose so.' Jason spoke reluctantly, as if he were
abandoning his companions.

'What good would staying here do?' said Bain. 'If
you can think of any one good reason why we should
remain prisoners, or how it would help the two Laceys,
I'd gladly stay.'

'No,' admitted Jason after some thought. 'I can't.'

'Well, then; that's settled. We'll start making a hole
in the roof after they lock us up for the night.'

Now that they had decided to make the attempt that
night the hours of daylight seemed to drag more slowly
than ever. The prisoners moved about restlessly, and
Jason grumbled: 'They're late with our mid-day tea!'

'They are – and I could do with another walk
round.' Bain got up from his blanket again and set his
eye to the nearest peep-hole.

'I'll give a shout,' suggested Jason. He was drawing a
good breath when Bain snapped: 'Hold it!' Face
pressed against the plank wall and his eye to the crack
he reported: 'There are some new people arriving,
more Shans by the look of them!'

'Where?' Jason sprang to the peep-hole to look out,
but could only see the space directly in front. He waited
impatiently, then at last the new arrivals came into
view, more than a dozen men in olive-green uniforms,
heavily armed and slung about with ammunition
pouches and in the middle of this file a laden mule. The
men were soaked with sweat, the mule's flanks were
striped dark and its head drooped. They stopped at a
great shout, and the huge bulk of the fat man came

lumbering down to meet them. 'It's Fatso,' reported Jason to Bain, who was squinting through one peep-hole after another trying to get a better view of the newcomers. 'He seems pleased to see them.'

'Can I look?' Bain took Jason's place. 'You're right – he's beaming all over his fat face. But he's not saying very much; they must be expected.' He crouched, murmuring to himself: 'Just what is that mule carrying?'

'Ammunition?' hazarded Jason. 'It must be heavy, for it looks pretty tired.'

'And it's a good strong mule, too,' said Bain. 'None of your country-bred stuff here – it's an imported Argentine by the size of it, and must have cost the Shans a good sum.' He stood back. 'You have another look, Jason; see what you make of it all.'

The clop of hooves, the creak of saddle leather and the clink of steel bit and bridle rings came closer as the small procession passed opposite the hut, and Jason concentrated on the mule's off-side load as the weary animal plodded past. He saw a sack holding two oblong metal shapes, all bound in a rope package and secured to the saddle hooks by rope eyelets – and then it was out of his range of sight.

He told Bain what he had seen. 'Nothing to identify, just some oblong tins wrapped up in a big sack.'

'Could they be as big as five-gallon kerosene tins?'

'Yes, I suppose they could.'

'I think they must be carrying dope in those tins, Jason – probably morphine. No wonder they escorted it!' He broke off to comment in a surprised voice:

'Those men are going straight back again – not even waiting for a cup of tea!'

'They looked in a hurry when they arrived,' agreed Jason.

'Not even a cup of tea ...' Bain was frowning. 'Things can't be too good for the Shans – which means that by sparing those men they were desperate to get that mule-load safe up here. I'm beginning to think there may be more than just morphine in those tins,' he said slowly.

'You mean heroin?'

'That would explain everything – why it was escorted up here by badly needed troops, why Fatso and his men were waiting for it, and why we were snatched. We are to be held hostage while that load is taken through the top corner of Thailand, probably into Laos. Unfortunately,' he sighed, 'we'll never know what those tins hold.'

Jason, however, was unconvinced. 'There's only one mule,' he pointed out. 'I know heroin's expensive, but surely that one load isn't worth all this trouble!'

'Well, now.' Bain stood up back from his observation hole. 'Let's just work it out.' Once again he was calm and precise. 'A load for a good mule in hill country is never more than a hundred and eighty pounds – that's roughly eighty kilos. We've seen that there are four of those big oblong tins, and they probably hold twenty kilos each of whatever it may be. It could also be gold,' he pointed out, 'or jade, for these Shans run both of those goods from Western China. But I'm guessing that it's dope of some sort because of the bulky tins.

Eighty kilos of gold would take up very much less room.'

'So we've got eighty kilos of something – say heroin.'

'I won't tell you what a single ounce fetches in New York, for I don't think you'd believe me, but I can tell you the latest round figure per kilo on the Bangkok wholesale market.' He paused, then said: 'Best quality heroin fetches twelve thousand dollars a kilo – multiply that by eighty.'

Jason was staggered. 'That's nine hundred and sixty thousand dollars!'

'The price keeps rising, so I think,' said Bain after a pause, 'that you could safely call that a million dollars' worth – more than the Golden Fleece ever was.' He smiled without any humour at all. 'Now do you see what's involved?'

'I see.' Jason whistled. 'Oh, yes, I see very well.'

'If it's morphine, of course,' Bain went on, 'it's not worth much more than a fifth of that – say two hundred thousand dollars.'

'Oh, nothing at all,' said Jason ironically.

'But still worth saving from the Burmese Army!'

'Thakin!' warned the guard outside and *thwack* went the mallet on the wooden bar. The door swung open, and the two prisoners were summoned out – but not, as they expected, to sit and drink tea. Instead they were led away from the hut down through the village gateway and ordered to sit out of sight of the village. 'Do you know,' said Bain thoughtfully. 'I think they've got us out of the way while they lock up that load in the store in our hut. Pity we can't see in.'

In front the forested hillside fell away, but in the

sliver of open terraced field immediately below them women moved about among the nearly waist-high poppies, stooping, busy a moment then moving on. Jason watched idly. 'What are they doing?'

Bain gave him an amused glance. 'What d'you *think* they're doing, you idiot? They're collecting opium!'

'Ah.' Jason sat up. 'So *that's* how they get it!' The nearest woman, ignoring the poppies which still wore their pink or white flowers, was working only on those topped with a naked, bulbous head, and Jason watched closely. She gripped and turned over one of the bulbs, and he saw blobs of sticky dark sap. These she scraped off with her knife and then into the small pot in her basket -- and in a moment was off to the next.

'This is her second visit to the field today,' explained Bain. 'She was here first thing this morning, nicking these bulbs to let the sap ooze out.'

'And that's opium?'

'That's opium, Jason, the cause of all the trouble.'

Jason said nothing. The woman was working swiftly, not looking up. Her black cotton jacket was damp with sweat, and she paused only to wipe her forehead before stooping over the next bulb. Bain caught Jason's expression and nodded. 'A hard life, boy. If only the opium lords could be made to work in the fields like this --' Then he was interrupted. The sounds of small-arms fire swelled up once again and drifted to them from the west, but it was louder and closer, and the two guards, till now so cheerful and friendly, eventually led the prisoners back, gave them tea and locked them up again in a gloomy silence.

'We'll rest this afternoon,' ordered Bain. 'You may not feel very sleepy, but try and doze off. We won't get much sleep tonight.'

Obediently Jason stretched out, covering his eyes with a fold of the red blanket. The light glowed faintly through the woollen threads and he remembered his dream with a grimace; it had been all too lifelike. For some time he lay there, his mind a jumble of thoughts, then at last dozed off, only waking when the door was thwacked open and they were brought their evening rice.

'Eat every grain of that,' advised Bain, and Jason forced himself to swallow, though he felt no hunger. When they had finished they were led out for another breather, but this time the guns to the west of them were silent.

'Perhaps the Burmese are moving round here!' said Jason with a nervous laugh.

'Perhaps.'

They spoke little as they walked up and down, and sat in silence when they were locked up again, listening to the women coming back from the poppy fields and the quiet sounds of the last half-hour of daylight.

Suddenly the peace of the evening was shattered. From beyond the ancestral gateway a light machine-gun opened up, firing into the village in fast, very long bursts, and a second joined in from the ridge. The three Shans smoking and chatting outside the hut sprang for cover, but the first guard was hit and fell back wounded near the hut door. 'The Burmese!' Bain shouted. 'They've made it!' and they flung themselves to the earthen floor. Through the uproar they heard the light pops of a grenade launcher, followed moments later by the thuds and bangs of grenades bouncing and exploding. Fragments rattled against the plank walls like vicious handfuls of gravel and they flinched and cowered as a cluster of bullet-holes suddenly appeared high up in the walls.

Keeping very flat Bain slid across to the nearest peep-hole, raised head and shoulders from the floor, squinted through hastily, then ducked down again. 'Can't see the Shans,' he shouted, 'but the Akhas are bolting.' Gingerly he eased himself up again, and Jason saw his neck muscles flinch as another burst passed very close by, then Bain turned round and roared: 'The sentry – he's out there behind the door! We can –' His voice was drowned in a different sound as firing broke out from under the Akha houses and bullets crackled back past them. Jason could hardly think. The shattering noise, the feeling of being trapped, the terrrifying force of the high-velocity weapons half-stunned him, and he blinked looking round for some way to escape, but saw only the strong plank walls of their prison quivering to the strike of bullets.

He dragged himself close to the wall and peeped out – just as firing swelled up across the open space. He ducked, looked again and saw a haze of cordite stand out and then spread and drift. 'The Shans are under that house,' Bain called to him and Jason, peeping hastily, saw Shans in ones and twos scuttle under the house opposite, settle behind the log supports and begin firing busily, spraying bullets down towards the gateway and back up towards the crest, with just visible the bulk of Fatso, bulging out on either side of a log beam.

'They won't be easily shifted!' Bain had his eye to a gap. 'They'll withstand a rush, for a bit anyway.' More grenades bounced and rolled and exploded in front of the house, but after each one the Shans bobbed up again, firing as determinedly as ever.

'The Burmese'll have to rush 'em,' grunted Bain, 'and if they approach from behind here . . .' He did not finish his sentence but Jason knew what he meant; anything that gave the attackers even the suggestion of shelter would draw immediate and heavy fire from the Shans – and their hut prison was one obvious line of approach. Behind him Bain was trying to see out to spot the Burmese, but without success, and Jason inched his head up again to look out towards the Shan defenders when suddenly he saw a grenade, thrown from somewhere nearby, come arching over and bounce from the roof of the house where they sheltered. But this was not one of the serrated brown high-explosive grenades but a cylindrical green canister. It landed fizzing below the verandah, and he called: 'Someone's in the houses behind them –' when it exploded. His eye caught, not the shock-wave of dust and flame of the smaller grenades but a bright red flash followed by a geyser of white particles, each tipped with glowing fire. He stared, calling, 'Look at that!' as the glowing particles showered down over the thatch and over the verandah which at once began to burn fiercely.

'Phosphorus!' Bain was beside him, staring. 'That'll –' His words were drowned in a confusion of shouts, shots and the crackle of flames. White smoke from the burning phosphorus particles and the dark smoke from the blazing thatch rose mingling in a heavy cloud, and below the house figures were springing up and beating at themselves. Chunks of burning thatch began falling through the blazing framework on to the floor below, and Jason heard a new noise – an intermittent popping, rather like gunfire. 'The heat's bursting the bamboo!' shouted Bain. 'Those Shans'll fry in there!' They stared at the indistinct figures under the blazing house; Jason wondered how anyone could remain in such an inferno, when, 'They're going!' shouted Bain. 'They're making a run for it!' He slapped Jason's shoulder. 'We're free, boy, free!'

Prudently they crouched down as far as they could while they watched running figures plunging away through the smoke and vanishing in the direction of the poppy fields and the jungle beyond. 'That's funny!' Bain cocked an ear, listening to the firing slacken. 'No cut-off gun? They're getting clean away!' As the Shans made their break the firing from the crest and gateway died away, and from the terraced fields behind came only a shout or two – but Jason did not worry; it was over. He got to his feet, drawing a deep, shaky breath and feeling able to look about for the first time without his muscles flinching in anticipation of a bullet-strike. He noticed, also for the first time, that in spite of the chill of approaching evening sweat had run down his ribs, soaking his shirt where it was tucked into his trousers.

'Here come the troops!' Bain was springing about peering through one peep-hole after another. 'They're moving down from the ridge, through the houses.'

For a moment Jason did not stir; he was not particularly interested in how the Burmese soldiers reached them, just that they had, and would soon open the door of their prison and let them go. 'They're being a bit cagey,' commented Bain. 'Perhaps they're worried about ambush.'

Jason put his eye to a crack and looked in the direction of the houses further up. Sure enough there were figures moving down, and he caught a glimpse between the houses, of crouching figures, dressed in dark clothing, about fifty or sixty yards away.

'There aren't too many of them,' said Bain, 'Maybe it was just a small patrol. No wonder they're being careful.'

Then Jason remembered: 'The Laceys!'

Bain whipped round. 'You're right!' He stared out again. 'Perhaps they went with the Akhas!' He spoke slowly, and Jason guessed what he was thinking: the firing from the ridge into the top end of the village had been heavy . . .

'Let's hope they got clear.' Bain looked very grim. 'They weren't exactly my cup of tea, that pair, but I'd be very sorry if anything happened to them. They were really dedicated to their work, really dedicated.' He stayed staring up into the houses, then spoke with a touch of alarm: 'That fire isn't getting any smaller.'

Jason saw what he meant: the house that had sheltered the Shans was burning fiercely and the thatch of the house next to it was beginning to scorch and smoulder. 'It's spreading,' he said, then found he had to raise his voice; 'It's spreading!'

A small, clear flame licked up the thatch, ran along the surface of the roof, seemed to die away – then with a whoosh and a roar the whole thatch burst into great reddish-yellow flames edged with dirty black smoke, and Jason felt a wave of hot air surge against his eye and stepped back, gasping and blinking.

Outside, the sky was now reddening with the sunset – or was it flames? A third house was now burning and again Jason heard noisy cracks of sections of exploding bamboo, as the heated air burst out of them.

'These blasted troops – wish they'd get a move on!' Bain was looking up at their own thatch, and Jason caught the suppressed anxiety in his voice as he added: 'Of course – they don't know we're here!'

Jason wiped the sweat from his face. He looked at the plank walls; if they caught light it might be possible to break them down – but the thatch would go first, then the opium next ... He sniffed; was there a warm, heavy scent drifting in from beyond that cupboard door?

'We'll give a yell,' commanded Bain. 'Ready?'

'AHOY!' They both shouted at the top of their lungs, 'AHOY! HELP!'

For good measure Bain hammered on the wall and Jason joined him, kicking at the planks with the side of his foot and yelling at the same time. Bain looked out: 'They've heard us!' He was staring out, but did not turn back to Jason. Instead he stayed crouching at a peep-hole. 'Scruffy-looking lot! However, they've done the job.' He stood up. 'There's a couple of them coming across.'

Outside they heard footsteps, a pause, muffled sounds, a thud or two, then the hammer-blows of the wooden beam being driven from its socket – and to Jason that racket sounded like music. He kept glancing anxiously up at the thatch; would it catch before the soldiers freed them? At last the beam was driven out and the door swung open; but whoever opened it had stepped back out of sight, and with a sign to Jason to wait Bain called: 'Hullo! Hullo there! We are prisoners!' Then he called out a phrase in Thai and very slowly walked out of the hut with his hands up, still talking reassuringly in English. From behind Jason saw him moving out, beyond him the background of collapsing, flaring beams and timbers. He saw Bain stop when well clear of the hut and turn smiling – and then saw the smile fade from his face.

Very slowly Jason walked out of the hut, hands up. He too looked about him and now saw the men who had released them. The nearest stood a little way back from the swung-open door. He wore a pair of calf-length and very ragged black trousers, a loose black bush jacket with webbing magazine pouches over this, and a sweat-stained felt hat – and he was covering them with an ancient, very worn and battered sub-machine-gun. He was small and fine-boned, his wheaten skin that of a Vietnamese or mixed-blood Chinese, and he had a small black moustache. Jason turned his head and looked at the other. He was of similar build, and similarly dressed, except that slung over his shoulder was a new automatic shotgun and in one hand the naked blade of a two-foot-long Burmese dah. Jason's eye travelled past him to where the wounded guard lay, close by the hut. No shotgun lay by him; instead, a deep sword-wound disfigured his throat.

Bain turned his head and Jason caught his eye – wary, and signalling to him to be very, very careful.

There was no indication as to who the captors of the village were, but one thing was certain: they were *not* the Burmese Army.

'And they've picked up the Laceys.' Bain jerked his head. Outside the ring of blazing houses the short twilight was fading, but inside it they stood illuminated by the shifting glare of the flames, and into this glare stumbled the Laceys and more of their captors, while another followed with the mule.

'It's out of the frying pan, Jason,' commented Bain resignedly. Jason, trying to complete the phrase, choked with a disappointment that was almost despair and could not utter a word – but the fire itself, now striding from roof to roof and beginning to beat in upon them more and more fiercely, provided its own reply.

# 5
## COOLIE

THE lull, exaggerated by the roaring flames and showers of sparks from the collapsing walls in front, was broken by an abrupt command from the shadows. At once the four Europeans were hustled to one side, the first two men hurried into the hut and there was the sound of battering at the inner door. Silent the prisoners listened, Jason with glum satisfaction: they couldn't open the door. But very quickly a third man came running up with one of the villager's mattocks, a flat chunk of iron on the end of a five-foot pole. He disappeared inside and there was the sound of smashing metal and splintering wood.

Bain seized the chance to whisper to Peter Lacey: 'How did they get you?'

'We ran for it – right into one of them.' Lacey licked his lips. He seemed uncomfortable, distraught even, and Meg looked at him, the whites of her eyes gleaming as she turned them in an intense sideways glance.

Jason felt uneasy; Lacey was not well, and it was no time to have a sick man with them. Hidden by the three men, Meg busied herself with her small shoulder-bag, and Jason saw firelight glimmer on phial and syringe. He glanced surreptitiously at their new guard; he was standing well back, but though his ancient automatic was covering them his eyes looked beyond at what the others were carrying out from the hut in a stare half of triumph, half of greed.

Two men were dragging out into the open the two sacks holding the oblong kerosene tins, still roped and hooked ready for the saddle-hooks. 'There goes the Golden Fleece, Jason,' murmured Bain out of the side of his mouth. Meg also heard him, and whispered back fiercely: 'But the Argonauts got it in the end!'

'Who are these people?' whispered Jason. 'They're nothing like the Shans!'

'They'll be Haus,' whispered back Bain. 'At least this first pair are. Here's their leader.' They stopped murmuring among themselves as a new figure appeared. He too wore black, carried a heavy auto-

matic pistol, and each of his waist pockets bulged with
what Jason guessed were grenades. His forehead was
bound with a strip of black cloth over which his long
black hair swept down over his ears and temples, two
lines of sweat ran down through the ash on his pale
cheeks like zebra stripes, yet no one smiled. He glanced
at the four bedraggled Europeans then turned away
without a word, as if they were of no account, and Jason
felt his heart sink. The leader gestured, the mule was
led up and two men lifted the sacks, hooked them on
and lashed the ropes over the top of the saddle.

'When I shout, run for your life,' murmured Bain to
Jason not moving his lips, 'pass it on.'

'Run when he shouts,' Jason muttered. He knew
what Bain meant. In the dark not all of them would be
hit, whereas if they stayed . . .

By their sudden withdrawn tension he knew the
others feared what he did – murder out of hand as a
nuisance and a source of information about the attackers.

There was a call from inside the hut, and two Haus
ran out with bags of opium. There was excited talk,
then they returned and began fetching out the white
bags from the store, while their leader stood studying
the growing pile.

'There's too much for the mule,' muttered the Scot.
'They'd cripple the beast if they overloaded it in this
kind of country.' He lapsed into silence as their guard
twitched his gun muzzle round, but Jason was watching
the leader, noting how a word from him brought instant
obedience. This was the man on whom their lives
depended. He held their fate in his hands; he could have

them slaughtered – or set free. He was a pale man, paler than the other Haus, though that could have been the effect of the grey-white ash and the glow of the fires. He spoke, two men ran off towards the houses still standing, and in a moment or two returned, also at a run, bringing large, cone-shaped baskets of the type Akha women used to carry firewood and containers of water.

A short burst of firing broke out somewhere down beyond the village gateway and ended as abruptly, a voice called urgently, there was more firing, it died away and the voice called again. Jason saw that the Haus had prudently left outlying pickets to cover themselves from wandering Shans while they raided the store and he breathed to Meg, crouched with an arm around Peter: 'It's just a sentry.' He tried to sound reassuring, but he heard his own voice waver. He cleared his throat. The Hau was still watching them carefully; there had been no chance to make a break for it, and Jason cursed the firelight – then his attention was drawn back to the men by the door. They were busily filling the cone-shaped baskets with the bags of opium, packing them in carefully until the heap had vanished, to be replaced by four heavy-looking baskets.

Jason looked round at the others. Like himself they had been watching the silent activities of the Haus – Bain with a kind of wry acceptance, Meg with a sullen awareness and Lacey, clear-eyed and normal again, with suspicion. Jason knew instinctively what was happening, and that the opium had saved them, for the moment at least. When the guard motioned to them to go forward and each pick up a basket, Jason stepped forward without protest.

He felt his shoulders gripped, two men swung a basket up against his back, the lower end of the cone resting against his hips and the wider part against his shoulders. They slipped a headband round the basket and up over his temples and let the weight of the basket settle.

Jason blinked. It was heavy, and he could feel the sharp edges of the woven wickerwork cut into his unaccustomed back muscles. His swimming muscles, thick and rubbery, took the strain easily, but the muscles lower down his ribs quickly began to feel the strain. Then, to his dismay, his hands were seized, clapped together and the wrists bound tightly with twists of fine cane strips. He stood there, a bound prisoner, loaded like a mule, but for the moment he accepted it; he was alive.

Then the others were hastily loaded, though he noticed that the Haus did not bind Meg, and one actually transferred some of her bags of opium to the baskets of the men. Ahead they saw the black outline of the loaded mule being hurried past the burning houses. They were prodded and waved on to follow, and Jason found himself in the lead. He leant his shoulders forward to prevent the basket from swinging, and with his bound hands grasped the woven cane headband. It pulled on his neck muscles, and he hunched himself up as best he could, leaning forward to try and get the point of balance of his load above the centre of his own body. It was awkward, for the strap was not quite the right length – but he knew it would be useless to try to have anything done by the Haus; their sense of urgency was too great. Their sparing use of words, the speed with which they worked, their forceful, unhesitating violence – all made it very clear that they were ruthless men in a hurry. Yes, the opium had saved them – but for how long?

The heat of the flames beat on them as they plodded past, and another house collapsed in showers of sparks. Ahead rose the ridge and beyond it, Jason knew, rose other ridges, each one steeper and higher. Where were they going, and what would happen when they got there? From the gateway came another quick burst of shooting, and the Hau behind Jason pushed at his basket, urging him to get a move on. 'I can't go any faster, you swine,' muttered Jason to himself. The man pushed the basket again and Jason stumbled. Recovering, he plodded on, but when the man again pushed him he swung round clumsily, bumping into him with the basket. 'Lay off,' he gritted in English, 'Lay off, will you.' The Hau stepped back in surprise, then with a quick grin of anticipation thumped the muzzle of his automatic hard into Jason's side, just behind the ribs.

'Uhh!' The sick pain that jolted through him and seemed to drive the breath out of his lungs made Jason exclaim in surprise. He staggered forward, conscious only of a hot spreading ache, when the Hau, with an accurate thrust, struck him once more, in the very same spot. This time Jason, shocked by the pain, could not cry out. Only one thing mattered to him – to hurry on, to escape those cruel, expert and unbelievably painful jabs. He stumbled on at a half run, the Hau following with a pleased smile. The basket swung unsteadily, tugging at his back muscles and cutting into him; the ridge path was steepening and his feet turned on loose rocks.

Behind him Jason could hear the faint anguished voices of the Akhas crying to each other as their homes burned, and dark figures ran about, but the flames only roared up higher, throwing a red glow over the ridge and lighting up the line of stumbling, loaded figures. A burst of firing broke out somewhere down in the darkness, bullets crackled over them, other weapons replied and a battle raged briskly behind them till they had topped the crest.

They were out of the light of the flames by now, and padding blindly through the night, but for Jason this was some relief, a small mercy, for the darkness hid his tears.

Dawn found them well along a tiny path on the far flank of the great ridge; it also found them near collapse. The Haus had allowed them a rest every thirty minutes – which eventually became twenty – but even so their pace grew slower and slower, in spite of the threats and urgings of their captors. When the Haus finally indicated a longer halt they flopped down at once and fell asleep sprawled out across the path.

To Jason it seemed no more than a moment before he felt himself roughly prodded by the toe of a canvas boot, and he opened his eyes to see the sun rising over the crest of yet another ridge before them. Again the boot prodded his ribs, with a groan he pushed himself to his feet and two Haus lifted the basket on to his back. He stood blinking and weary under the load of opium, watching as the others were similarly roused and loaded, but he felt one slight relief: with the warmth of his back the wicker basket seemed to have moulded itself to him, no longer cutting in. He also noticed, though without caring, that he, as were the others, was stained where sweat had soaked into the nearest bags and the sappy opium had run, leaving dark brown patches down the sides of their shirts. He still felt the ache in his side where the gun muzzle had jabbed him, and he leant over slightly as he stood, to keep the basket from pressing against the spot.

With the four prisoners up and loaded the little convoy was about to move off when there was an exclamation, and Jason felt his wrist seized. He looked down. The sun's rays, flashing across the tree-tops, glittered on the steel of his watch, and he stood with dull resentment as his hands were quickly unbound and the watch – a fifteenth birthday present from his parents – was dragged off and slipped on to a Hau wrist, and his hands were tied again.

There was a babble of talk and one by one the others were relieved of their watches, and then their pockets searched. Angus Bain's pen and penknife were seized with exclamations of satisfaction, as was the Thai money in a small leather note-case in his hip pocket. From the corner of his eye Jason caught a swift movement by Meg; while the Haus were occupied in searching Peter Lacey she slipped something unobtrusively in among the opium bags in her basket. Then his attention was jerked back to Peter himself who cried out: 'No! My medicine – don't take it! Please don't take it!'

A Hau stood with a flat plastic case in his hands, looking with angry disappointment at a row of small ampoules of clear liquid. 'Medicine,' said Peter Lacey huskily. His eyes were fixed on the open case, as if hypnotized, then with an effort he looked up beseechingly at the Hau, and made the motion of swallowing something. 'Medicine,' he half-whispered. 'Please.' He raised his bound hands and the Hau, looking at the case and then at Peter, stepped back, holding it away. The heavy basket still on his back, Peter sank to his knees again, raised his hands to the Hau but he held the case a little higher and away, watching Peter's face.

By now everyone else, Haus, prisoners, even the aloof leader some yards further on, had stopped to watch.

'I'll get it, Peter.' With her eyes fixed on the man with the case Meg walked forward towards him. Hands out and talking reassuringly, as though to someone reasonable and sensible, she said: 'Will you give that to me? I'll look after it, for Peter really needs his medicine.'

The Hau waited till she was close to him, then with his free hand gave her a push that sent her staggering back against Jason. Then, eyes still on Peter's anxious face, the Hau dropped the case to the path, put his foot down and ground the ampoules to pieces and at Peter's despairing cry he smiled, while the others laughed amongst themselves.

There was an abrupt command from the leader. He rose and without a backward glance set out along the path. The Haus behind grunted to the prisoners to go on, but Lacey, slumped on his knees, did not move.

'Peter!' Meg whispered across at the kneeling figure, head sunk on his chest, while Jason watched with sick pity. 'Peter,' she whispered urgently: 'I've still got the syringe, and one from last night.' He looked up, blinking.

'Yes.' She gave him a fractional nod of the head, and slowly he struggled up.

They walked for an hour, plodding along the tiny winding path through patches of forest and occasional open spaces where head-high grass grew, but their pace was draggingly slow, and at the next halt the four sank down in a stupor of exhaustion, only to be roused again in a few minutes.

'I don't think I can go any further,' said Meg. 'And if they drive Peter on much more he'll die. He's in bad shape.'

Bain looked up warily at the Haus standing waiting for them. 'It's march, Meg, or maybe die here.' He pushed himself to his knees, dragged round his basket and slung the headband on. 'Hup we go!' Seeing Meg sit unmoving, her mouth turned down in determination, he pivoted slowly round towards Jason. 'Here, lad – you get up,' he commanded, and Jason, hearing the edge in his voice, an edge sharp with desperate urgency, staggered up and heaved the basket on to his back. 'Now, Meg,' ordered Bain. 'Take some of those opium bags from Peter's basket and put them into mine. I'll tell you when to stop – and Jason can take a couple, can't you Jason?'

'Yes.' Jason felt numb, his legs and thighs leaden, his feet, skinned and burning, as if they belonged to some other Jason, someone suffering in another existence. 'Yes,' he said. 'I can take some.' He stood there, bowed, waiting patiently for the additions to his load, when 'No,' said Meg from the ground. 'I won't do that.' Holding Peter Lacey's bound hands she lay staring up at Bain. '*You* can do what these people want, *I* won't.'

'They'll shoot you, Meg,' he warned, adding more gently: 'It won't be for long, then we'll have a good rest. They just want to get clear of the Shans!'

'They're going to shoot us all anyway,' she said calmly. 'Let them do it now and they can carry their opium themselves.'

One of the Haus, a man with a pock-marked face, walked closer and tapped her basket. She gave him a calm look and shook her head slowly. He pushed at the basket with the muzzle of his gun and spoke curtly, and still she lay there, leaning back against the basket and shaking her head from side to side. He pointed the automatic at her and she lay looking back at him.

'He's going to shoot!' Bain stepped forward awkwardly under his load to try and pull the Hau away and another ran back along the path cocking his weapon as he came.

'Go on,' said Meg to the Hau aiming at her. 'Shoot. Go on.'

His finger tightened round the trigger and Jason closed his eyes, waiting for the short burst, the scatter of cartridge cases, the sudden corpse . . . He opened his eyes again. The Hau, showing his teeth, was now staring at Angus Bain, who swung off his basket and dumped it on the path. '*You* carry it,' he said, and sat down beside Meg. His words may have been incomprehensible to the Haus, but his actions were not, and another came running down, and aimed his weapon at Bain.

Then Jason heard his own voice saying: 'Carry it yourselves.' He swung off the basket and let it fall with a crash, the opium bags spilling out across the path. He sat on the ground, hunched up, waiting for the blow, the beating, the jolt in the kidneys again, and he trembled; he'd rather be shot and get it over with. He gritted his teeth and shut his eyes. This was it; the Haus would soon see they weren't going to move and would shoot the lot of them. After all, he'd heard Bain say that the opium was worth only a fraction of the heroin, if that was what it was, and they had a mule for that, a mule that wouldn't complain . . . His hands felt the earth on which he sat, dry and dusty, like his throat. He wished they'd hurry up and get it over.

Nothing happened. Jason opened his eyes. A little way along the path the leader stood looking back down at them. He spoke briefly, and turned and walked away again. The two Haus stepped back and lowered their weapons. One of them shook Bain by the shoulder and, indicating his watch, held up one finger. 'An hour's rest,' said Bain, then shook his head. 'Not enough.' He held up three fingers and the Hau called something angrily – and at the reply nodded, walked away and sat facing back along the way they had come.

'They either want the opium pretty badly,' said the Scot, 'or they're very greedy – or they want us! Now, which is it? What do you think, Jason?'

But this last query Jason did not hear. Head back, mouth half open, he was sleeping heavily.

*

The prod in the ribs was not gentle. Jason muttered;
the bright daylight hurt his eyes and he turned over,
careless of the discomfort of leaning his head against the
wickerwork, only to be prodded again, more insistently,
and he also heard Angus Bain some yards away saying:
'Time to go, Jason, time to get up, wakey, wakey –' and
Jason sat up.

The Hau prodding him with his automatic stepped
back and pointed to the basket, and as Jason blinked
awake – still feeling as if he had just that moment gone
to sleep – he realized that at least it was not cold. He
scrambled up, half-hoping that it had all been rather a
nasty dream, and that he would wake up – he thought
with a shock of disbelief – safely back with the Shans.
He looked anxiously about. He was consumed by
thirst, his throat was now so dry that he could barely
speak and he asked huskily: 'Have they any water?'

'No water.' Bain stood with his basket on, the headband round his temples. 'We're still above the streams,
but the path goes down the next ridge.'

Peter Lacey was slowly and painfully adjusting the
strap of his basket and Jason realized that here was one
person, at least, in worse case than himself. Meg stood
nearby with her load, and mechanically he said: 'Can
I take some of your opium?' She shook her head.

'Here we go.' Bain led off as the Haus waved. 'Just
keep it steady, everyone.'

Jason felt stiff for the first few minutes, stiff and
painful and thirsty, but his eyes no longer prickled with
lack of sleep and the sun warmed them. But where were
they going? The constricting headband and the pull of
the load kept him leaning forward, head downwards,

but he was able to see by twisting his head sideways. They were heading east for a razor-backed ridge with a village prominent below the crest of it, surrounded by terraced poppy fields. Jason guessed that the secondary path they followed would take them out by that village. Was it a Hau village? Perhaps it was full of Shans, and if so would they be ambushed as they toiled up the slope towards it? These speculations flitted through his mind and as quickly out again; he was conscious only of an overpowering thirst, and he wondered how he could sweat so copiously, great drops rolling from beneath the headband.

Down they went, the vegetation changing and becoming denser in the growing dampness of the ravine, but they struggled on for another quarter of an hour before reaching the first tiny runnels of a stream. The four prisoners shrugged free of their loads, flung themselves down and began scooping up water into their mouths. 'Hiyah!' cried one of the Haus in warning as the mule also plunged down, dragging him along in spite of his tugs and jerks, till it splashed into the stream and stood with its forelegs in the water, drinking deeply.

'Don't drink too much, Jason.' Bain pushed himself back, wiping his mouth, and water glistened on the black stubble of his jaw. Jason sat back, feeling the water splash inside him. He *had* drunk too much, and now felt uncomfortably full.

'Ha!' One of the Haus motioned with his automatic, pointing at the tumbled basket, and Jason picked it up, set it against the slope and began rearranging the opium bags inside with his bound hands. When he had finished he looked at them; they were puffy and red, and the tight cane bindings were cutting into his wrists deeper than ever. He felt sorry for his hands. He examined them dispassionately; if the bindings weren't cut soon the flesh would swell up so much round them it would be difficult even to cut them loose, let alone untie them.

All round the dip where the path cut across the stream Haus and prisoners were sprawled untidily, and it came to him that the Haus must be very nearly as tired as they were. They would have made a long march to reach the Akha village, then they had made their attack, and had then marched back. It was true they weren't carrying anything except their own weapons and the bits and pieces of loot, but they had still been hard at it for many hours.

The sun was invisible through the trees but an occasional short shadow showed that it must be nearly mid-day. Bloated with water the prisoners leant silently against their baskets – Jason beginning to drowse off again, Peter Lacey with his eyes shut and his face the colour of putty, Meg bedraggled but watchful and Bain looking up towards the Haus. 'I think we may be getting something to eat,' he said slowly. 'At least,' he corrected himself, 'the Haus are going to have something to eat.' Across the little stream one man was building a small fire, a second knelt washing rice in a very black, very dented and battered aluminium cooking pot, which he then set to boil on the fire, propped on two stones.

'They don't seem worried about the Shans trying to get that mule-load back,' commented Meg.

'I've been thinking the same.' Bain jerked his head in the direction of the leader, seated by himself beyond the fire, legs tucked under him and contemplating the forested slope below. 'But he seems to have it all worked out; there'll be no Shan pursuit.'

'Well – why not?'

'Simple,' replied Bain. 'Fatso hasn't enough men.'

'Fatso?' Meg raised an eyebrow.

'The big Shan.'

'Oh, you mean Maung Kyaw!' She gave a twisted smile. He gave her a puzzled glance, but after a fractional pause went on: 'He had seven or eight men to begin with, but at least one was killed last night, one or two would have been burnt by that phosphorus grenade, and others maybe wounded earlier. Fatso's in no condition to follow. Suppose he walks into an ambush? He can't do much except send for help – and the others are busy with the Burmese Army. They might spare a few men if they want that mule-load back badly enough, but even then they'll have a bit of a job.'

'Why?'

'He doesn't know who attacked him! They could have been any one of a dozen small gangs. No,' he shook his head. 'We'll get no pursuit from the Shans.'

'So we must save ourselves.' Meg looked across to the cooking fire and the steam beginning to rise from the pot of rice.

To their astonishment, and before the Hau sitting guarding them could move, Meg rose, crossed the stream and took from a surprised cook the pan in which he was mixing a paste of dried fish and chillies. The guard ran after her and Jason winced in anticipation, expecting to see her receive one of those cruelly expert blows, but she ignored him and calmly went about the business of setting the pan to fry at one end of the fire. The guard, weapon poised to club her, hesitated, perhaps baffled by her unconcern as she worked busily, and looked indecisively towards the black-clothed leader, immobile except for a turn of the head towards the strange tableau by the fire. After a long stare he turned his head away again and resumed his contemplation of the slope below. The Hau lowered his weapon and stepped back.

'We-ell!' Bain let out a long breath. Jason blinked in relief and Peter Lacey sank back against his basket. Across the stream Meg examined the rice and busied herself stirring the pungent fish paste bubbling in the pan, while sitting on the slope above the other Haus, at first glowering and suspicious, watched her with curiosity and then with grins.

She signalled that the food was ready and one by one the Haus, still grinning, came bringing large leaves plucked from the huge aspidistra-like plants that grew near the stream. All except one; the leader did not move, indeed made no sign of having any thought for the food. Meg hesitated, then she plucked a leaf, heaped it with rice and paste and took it to him, closely watched by two of the Haus. He gave no sign of noticing her presence and, after a longer hesitation, Meg bent and laid the leaf-platter with its steaming contents on the ground before him. He ignored the food till she had moved back to the fire, then, with almost abstracted movements, began to eat.

'That leader of theirs doesn't muck in with the others,' muttered Bain in a low voice. 'Keeps himself aloof, as though' – he paused – 'as though he's not actually one of them.'

Peter Lacey, slumped down in the gloom, made no reply, but Jason whispered back: 'You mean he's not a Hau?'

'That's right. They don't seem to chat with him, maybe because they have to use broken Burmese. And he didn't join them in looting us, or baiting Peter with his medicine – or thumping you, Jason.'

'I don't care what he is,' Jason's whisper was unsteady. 'Just so long as he lets us have something to eat!'

With pathetic intensity the prisoners watched, then Meg came across with the pot and the frying pan – now with no more than a glance from the Haus sitting eating higher up the slope. 'Hands out!' They raised their bound wrists, hands open, and she scooped out a handful of rice each, topped off with fish paste. They gobbled it down. Meg came round once again, then put the pot down. 'That's the lot, I'm afraid.'

Bain, licking the last grains of rice from his palms, said sharply: 'You haven't had a single bite yourself!'

'Just keep quiet. I'm going to give Peter his injection while these Haus are eating.' Moving about, apparently giving the prisoners the last of the rice, Meg busied herself behind her basket, and while the other two pretended to be scraping out the pot and sharing out non-existent rice, she signalled to Peter. He edged over and there was the quick flash of needle. 'There.'

'All right?' asked the correspondent, without turning his head.

'Yes.' Meg sighed. 'That's the last dose.'

'We'll have to get away, but I can't think how. Oh – here we go again.' A Hau came slithering down the slope, beckoning them to load up. Meg nudged the man beside her. 'Come on, Pete, time to go.'

Lacey opened his eyes and pushed himself briskly to his feet, and Jason marvelled at the quick effects of the injection; half an hour earlier Peter Lacey had looked quite finished. The four helped each other on with their baskets, now an automatic task. Ahead of them the mule stood by the stream, head drooping, and Bain scowled. 'The brutes haven't off-loaded that animal since last night.'

They climbed steadily, following the tiny winding path uphill, the handful of food restoring a little of their flagging strength. At the frequent halts for rest the men flopped down, but Meg, her basket laid aside, took to wandering just off the path among the bushes and tangled vegetation that grew rampant in the patches where the sunlight struck through. At first the two guards watched her suspiciously, Moustache in particular looking as if he were quite ready to shoot, but soon they paid her little attention and made no effort to prevent her moving about. Between the halts, however, it was steady climbing, and by mid-afternoon they reached the fringes of the poppy fields they had seen that morning from the far hillside. The loaded prisoners were exhausted again and filled with foreboding, and Jason found that he forgot his physical pain – the swollen wrists, the aching back where he had been struck by Moustache and the burning pain in the soles of his feet — in the duller fear of what awaited them when they reached their destination.

Instead of following the path up towards the village, however, they turned aside and skirted the terraced poppy fields, moving slowly while one of the Haus walked well ahead, regularly signalling back that all was clear. Jason managed a quick glance at the village as they passed below it; in size and layout it resembled the Akha village, although the angle of roofs and general construction of the houses seemed slightly different. After a long detour they reached the ridge beyond, and for a hundred yards or so they followed the path downhill, and with a flicker of hope Jason calculated that they must be heading south again, in the direction of Thailand. Then they reached another tiny path which turned off and plunged down eastwards, and above the tree-tops they caught the flash and glitter of water. Bain muttered round at him: 'The Mekong,' and Jason's hopes died.

# 6

## NIGHT

THE river was no more than four hours' march below them, but it was only too obvious that they would not reach it that night. Already the shadows of the ridge lay along their path, and the chill of approaching evening touched their skins. Jason, plodding along numbly, knew that another cold night awaited them,

but not a night of walking. He could walk no more.
Neither, it appeared, could Peter Lacey. From behind
Jason came a stumbling crash. He plodded on a few
paces, then swung round under his basket to see Peter
lying on his face, the basket overturned on top of him
and white bags of opium spilled across the path. The
pock-marked Hau, showing anxious irritation, was
prodding Lacey, and Meg, basket thrown aside, turned
him over. He was breathing in unsteady gasps, mouth
open and face mottled. One or two Haus came running
back, and one took Lacey's basket, repacked it and
slung it on himself. Now they'll shoot him, thought
Jason – but another of the Haus lifted the semi-
conscious Peter and helped him along down the path.

'You all right, Jason?' asked Bain in a low voice.
'Can you keep going for a bit longer?'

'Yes.' Jason answered mechanically. 'Yes, I can
keep going.' His legs were beginning to tremble with
strain. It was almost a relief to move on again.

They did not have to go far, for very soon the
straggling column had reached a small dip in which
flowed one of the many small jungle streams, and here
the Haus prepared to make camp. First, they unloaded
the mule, lifting down the two sacks to the ground on
either side of it but not bothering to unsaddle. Next
they secured the prisoners, running a length of split
rattan cane through between their bound wrists and
fastening it round a tree. Meg they ignored, and Bain
muttered: 'They know, somehow, she won't leave
him.' Peter Lacey was beginning to stir again, and
after seeing he was breathing normally Meg whispered
to the others: 'Let's pray they cook again.'

'Yes – and this time *you* get something to eat!'

'It's not that, Angus.' Meg's hard expression did not change. 'Your talk of the Golden Fleece last night gave me an idea, and I've been turning it over all day. You ought to know this one, Jason: how did the first Jason get the Fleece away?'

Jason blinked at her; was she beginning to wander? But the story, ingrained in him since childhood, swam back from the depths of his memory. Almost too tired to feel curious any longer he said in a flat, weary voice: 'For love of Jason the enchantress Medea, the keeper of the dragon that guarded the Fleece, drugged it with a magic potion, allowing Jason to climb the ash tree and carry off the Fleece.'

'We've no magic potions, but I've managed to get hold of an ordinary one.'

Bain broke in: 'So that's why –'

'I did the cooking?' She smiled ironically. 'Yes, I didn't do it to help them. Now listen,' she commanded, contriving at the same time to look as if she was saying nothing of importance. 'I'll try cooking again but one of *you* get out about a thumbnail of opium from one of those bags. Don't get caught. I'll make some excuse to come back for it. And no one is to touch the fish paste.'

Without opening his eyes Peter Lacey said in a tired voice: 'Opium raw won't knock them out.'

'No, but mixed with this it will.' She opened her hand. In her palm lay what looked like small pale chilli seeds. 'Datura Fastuosa; it's growing wild over half Asia, and here too.'

'Datura and opium! Of course!' muttered Bain.

'That's what the Thugs used when they doped and strangled travellers.'

'Yes. I began to see the plants once we were away from the higher ground.'

'Won't they smell it, or taste it?'

'Not in this fish paste, they won't!'

Peter spoke again, this time leaning up on an elbow. 'Be careful, Meg; you want narcosis, not vomiting.'

'I'll be careful.' She rose. 'Get that opium.'

Meg had barely taken two paces when the Haus on the slope above abandoned their camp-making and snatched up their weapons. Jason, slumped against the tree as if quite indifferent to what was going on, watched with a sense of hopelessness, but Meg, ignoring the muzzles aiming down at her, walked steadily on, gesturing towards the man who had lit the fire at their last halt, and pointing towards the blackened cooking pot tied with cord to his roll of blanket. His face hard with suspicion the Hau hurried down, and Jason closed his eyes: Meg was going to be grabbed, perhaps beaten, certainly hustled back to where the other prisoners lay and tied up herself – and that would be the end of their escape attempt. He listened for the curt command, the flat crack of a steel barrel against flesh, the shocked gasp of pain, but heard nothing and in a moment or two opened his eyes. He let out a long breath of relief and surprise: Meg was calmly gathering sticks for the fire while the Hau was climbing the slope again and untying his cooking pot.

Then Bain whispered: 'Jason, your basket's nearest – can you get a bag out without being spotted?'

'I'll try.' He eased himself back towards the basket,

lying half on its side beside the path, but found that the rattan line which linked the three of them checked him. 'Give me more of this thing,' he whispered. The others shifted closer to the tree and Jason felt the line give. He moved again and felt the wicker basket against his back. He sat there for a moment, heart thumping, feeling the warm softness of the opium as he leaned against it. From where he sat he could see Meg washing the rice; behind her the fire was blazing up and the Haus were again busying themselves with their sleeping places and Jason took another deep breath. Soon she'd be putting that pot of rice on the fire, and then would be her chance to come across on some pretext; if he were late their chance would be lost for good.

Bain, too, was worried: 'How's it going, Jason?' In spite of his forcedly casual question a note of anxiety crept in: 'Can I do anything?'

'Keep an eye on the Haus.' Jason put his arms up as though to rub an ear. 'Give me a whisper if they start looking down here.'

He had reckoned without Meg. She was making great play with the fire, moving about busily, occasionally leaning back to wave smoke out of her eyes, now kneeling to blow on an ember, now sitting back with an expression of concern at the amount of water in the pot – and the Haus, their sleeping places ready, one by one sat back to watch her.

'Right,' whispered Bain. 'Now's your chance!'

Jason stretched his bound hands back over his shoulder, pushed himself back hard against the basket and felt his finger-tips brush against the bunched folds of the top of a bag. He closed his fingers, they did not grip, he strained back harder, then felt the bag mouth firmly between his fingers. He dug his nails into the linen, drew it gently over and snatched it down between his legs. For a moment he could not speak, then in a thick voice he hardly recognized said: 'Got it!'

'Watch out!'

A Hau came sliding down the slope, jumped the last two or three feet to the path, walked towards the three prisoners – and stepped over their sprawl of legs and walked on past towards the rearguard sentry. In a few minutes this man appeared, humming in a high, wavering falsetto. He looked at the prisoners, as if seeing them for the first time, grinned and, resuming his high-pitched hum, passed them and climbed up the slope towards the others.

'Phooooo!' Jason heard Bain blow out his cheeks. 'Quick – can you open it?'

'It's stitched!' Jason fumbled at the compact, oblong bag. 'It's sewn up with something!'

'Use your teeth!'

From the corner of his eye Jason caught movement, Meg coming towards them; she'd be at the tree in a few more slow paces and the Haus would be watching – but they'd be watching her. He lowered his head, seized a thread with his teeth, bit, pulled – and felt it give. 'Okay,' he gasped, 'it's open!'

'Get some out, about a thumbnail of it. Get ready to pass it to her.' Bain's voice was calm and reassuring.

'All right.' One corner of the bag was open, but the opium inside was still covered over by stitched folds of cloth. He squeezed, nothing happened, he squeezed

harder – and fragments of sticky blackish brown paste
edged with a crumbly dried crust burst between the folds.

'A thumbnail-worth,' said Bain, eyeing the Haus. 'Be
ready.' He jerked his head very slightly and Meg,
ignoring the Haus, walked across, leant over Peter
Lacey and pulled from his pocket a handkerchief, with
which she ostentatiously wiped her face and neck – but
stretched her other hand towards Jason. He thrust into
it fragments of the half-dried opium and she rose,
again with casual slowness and, still mopping herself,
walked back towards the fire.

Jason sat still, wondering what to do next. He was
awkwardly placed, sitting with a partially opened bag of
opium between his thighs, and tell-tale fragments on
the ground.

'She's ready to dish up.'

The light was fading and the flames from the cooking
fire, ruddy now, lit up Meg's intent face as she examined the rice, then she straightened up and waved to the
Haus. Obediently they came down the sloping hillside,
each plucking his own leaf-platter, and when they
reached the fire Meg scooped out the rice for them and
added to each a dollop of the savoury mess of fried fish
and chillies, and Jason seized the opportunity to push
the opium bag back over his shoulder into the basket.
Meg sent one Hau with food to the sentry while she
took the same ration of rice and fish to where the leader
sat alone, cross-legged above the path. He glanced
round as she approached and Jason, tense and fearful,
saw the pale face, its swathing of black merging with the
dark background, as if disembodied, hanging in the
air. He shivered; touched by memory of someone.

But Meg was walking back with just the right touch of weariness. She paused a moment at the fire, gesturing towards the prisoners, and one Hau gave an irritated wave of the hand, as if to say: 'Don't trouble us, woman, just get on with it,' and once again Meg carried the pot across. 'Hands out,' she commanded, in exactly the same tone as before, and she carefully gave each the exact ration. She returned to the fire, on the way giving the last of the rice to the mule, then set about scrubbing out the cooking pot with handfuls of earth from the stream bank and rinsing it thoroughly in the trickle of running water. She returned it to its owner, he grinned, and at last she came back to the prisoners' tree and sank down with every appearance of settling down to sleep.

A yard or two away the mule shifted, a vague outline against the trees. Above them the Haus were stretching out and matches spurted as they lit cigarettes after their meal.

'Did they eat it?' Jason's whisper was uneven.

'I think so,' she whispered back.

'Do you think it will work?' He knew it was a stupid question, but could not resist asking it.

'We'll soon find out.'

'H'm – but any idea how long we should give them?' Bain asked.

'Half an hour at least. If they've taken the opium they'll sleep more and more heavily, if not they might fall asleep anyway.'

'We're still tied.'

'If they pass out I'll get one of their dahs.'

'Here – look at him!' Bain hissed at them.

Down the slope came a dark figure, in one hand a
glowing cigarette. He stumbled and came slithering
down, reached the path and stood swaying. Jason stared
up at him. He could not make out his features, but he
knew the outlines of their captors, and this one looked
like the second of the men who had opened the door of
their hut in the Akha village. He mumbled something
down at them, lifted his cigarette in a wide, careless arc
and the glowing end brightened as he took a deep draw
at it. He swayed, yawned noisily and started to climb
the bank again but sat down suddenly a yard or two
away, his cigarette flaring as he puffed at it spasmodic-
ally.

'He's taken his lot, all right,' whispered Bain.

Then the hand holding the cigarette fell and they
watched anxiously. Would it burn him and wake him
up?

'I'll get it away.' Meg stretched out, plucked the stub
from his fingers and squashed it out. The men above,
indistinct shapes in the dusk, made no move.

'He's out.' Meg's whisper, till now so steady, was
uneven. 'I'll get his dah.' A blade scraped from a
wooden scabbard. 'I've got it. You first, Angus.' There
was silence for a moment as Meg worked till she
whispered: 'That cane string's sunk right in.'

'Hold on, I'll pull my wrists apart a bit more. Now
try.'

'Tell me if I cut you.'

Jason listened. Once Bain suppressed a grunt, then
he sighed: 'They're free.' Jason heard the faint sound
of rubbing, and Bain whispered: 'Meg, you cut the
boy loose. My hands are numb.'

Jason held up his bound wrists and felt Meg's hand come out and take them. 'Try not to make a sound.'

He clenched his teeth. The edge of the long blade explored along the bindings, and each prod and bit of pressure brought stabs of pain.

'Hang on, Jason,' muttered Meg between her teeth. 'Hang on, it's giving.' She exerted all her force and at last, the cane bindings parted.

At first he felt only relief, but then followed an atrocious tingling, pins and needles of such intensity that he felt like crying. The pain as the blood flowed back into his hands seemed almost unbearable, and he rocked back and forth in the darkness. He tried putting his hands in his armpits, but even that faint pressure was too much and he waited blindly, elbows on knees and hands out before him for the pain to go away.

'Are you all right, Jason?' Meg heard his harsh, unsteady breathing. 'Is it your hands?'

He could not bring himself to speak, simply hissed affirmation. 'It'll pass in a little while,' she consoled. 'It won't take long.'

'Wheesht!' They stopped moving. Above them they heard an inarticulate grunt, the faint crackle of leaves as a heavy body turned over, then silence again. It was quite dark, except for the faint glow from the dying embers occasionally obscured as the mule, head drooping and standing awkwardly on the slope, shifted its weight.

'All right.' They breathed again. 'Now you, Peter,' said Meg, and at last, he too was free.

'Wait here.' Bain rose to a crouch. 'I'll check on the sentry.'

'But –'

'We've got to get past him sometime.' He vanished into the darkness, long moments passed, then came a hiss: 'Here, Peter – the shotgun. Safety catch above the trigger guard. All right?'

'All right,' Peter whispered back, and Jason caught the faint glimmer of firelight on a steel barrel.

'He's out cold. Take Meg, get up to the ridge. We'll meet there. Go on, now.'

Peter and Meg crept away along the path. For a moment or two Jason heard hesitant, careful footsteps, then there was silence.

'Jason.' Bain gripped his shoulder. 'Hands better?'

'Yes.'

'Listen. I'm going to take the mule –' At Jason's involuntary start he gripped his shoulder harder. 'Listen,' he hissed. 'I'm not leaving that dope for them. I'm going to load that animal, and take it with me, but I could do with a hand to load her.'

Jason, fearing that any moment furious Haus would wake and spring down on them, felt like seizing Bain and dragging him away. Misinterpreting his silence, Bain said, 'You go on, then. Tell the others.'

Torn between the urge to put as much distance as possible between himself and the Haus, and the frightful shame of leaving this lunatic in the lurch, Jason hissed angrily: 'All right, then!'

'You sure? Good. I'll just get this chap's Sten gun.' Bain groped across to the snoring figure and there was a clink of metal. 'Now for the mule.'

He approached with a warning click of the tongue, ran his finger down the girths and tightened the girth

straps, then whispered: 'One side at a time.' Between
them they swung up the first sack, and while Jason
supported it Bain hooked on the rope eyelets. 'Other
side.' With two of them the loads swung up easily.
Jason felt a stab of pity for the animal which stood so
patiently.

'You go ahead, Jason. I'll follow. Any shooting,
vanish!'

'All right.' Jason began making his way forward at a
half-crouch, hands before him, but in a few moments he
stopped. A darker patch lay humped against the slope –
the sentry. Jason waited, not daring to move, though he
kept saying to himself that the others must have passed
him. At length, after what seemed an interminable
wait but in reality could have been no more than a
minute, he heard a faint but very distinct snore. He
moved forward again, at an awkward sliding shuffle,
tensed to spring down into the undergrowth below –
then he was past, and with every step felt his breathing
steady, till another worry entered his mind: had the
others turned uphill already? Was he simply creeping
on into the forest, away from the ridge and the path?

'Jason?' The whisper took him by surprise and he
crouched, then recognized Meg's voice. 'Yes – Angus
is coming behind.' He sat down carefully. Lacey and
Meg were whispering and he caught a fragmentary
phrase or two: '– river . . . the Thai side . . . Maung
Kyaw . . .'

Jason jerked up his head. In spite of the cold, their
frightful danger and his total ignorance of their whereabouts, he was nodding off. He rubbed his eyes, but
his head was sinking down on his chest again when the

creak of leather saddlery and the tremor of hoofbeats
startled him wide awake. Bain whispered to them from
the dark: 'All right?'

'What –!' Lacey gasped in total surprise. 'You've
brought the mule!' He seemed to find difficulty in
speaking. He gasped again and Jason heard the disbelief in his voice. 'The mule! You've brought the
mule!'

'Yes, it hadn't been off-saddled – we got the loads on
easily enough.' His whisper was breathless but confident. 'Let's go – back up and round that village. Got
that shotgun all right?'

'What's the idea, Angus?' Meg's whisper held real
dismay. 'They're bound to follow, and then they'll
slaughter us!'

'They were going to do that anyway.' He led off
again, and Lacey scrambled aside as the mule's hoof
came down perilously near his foot. 'Sorry,' said Bain
curtly, 'but we can't wait.'

Jason plodded along behind. His wrists were still
sore, his bruised side still ached, he was more weary
than he had ever been in his life – but these were all
outweighed by one fact: for the moment, at least, he
was free.

Their first moment of real terror came when a dog
barked some two hundred yards below the path. 'Must
be the village!' Bain stopped and Jason blundered
straight into the mule. The barks swelled to a noisy
chorus as other dogs joined in.

'Are we going the right way?' demanded Peter.

'Don't know,' mumbled Jason. He stood leaning

against the mule's hindquarters, getting what comfort he could from the warm, sweating flanks.

'Don't fall asleep!' Bain prodded him. 'Not much farther. We'll get past the village and lie up tonight beyond the poppy fields. Come on.'

The next half hour seemed a waking nightmare. Each pebble on the path seemed the size of a boulder – and a boulder precariously perched, ready to roll and twist unwary ankles – and the ridge seemed to grow ever steeper. At last Bain halted again. 'We'll turn down, now,' he whispered. 'Stick close.'

He pushed through the short undergrowth edging the path and leading the mule by the full extent of the rein, slithered and stumbled down till he landed heavily in the first field. 'Keep along the edge,' he whispered as the others slithered down after him. 'Don't trample the crop, or the villagers'll spot it in the morning.' He pushed along beside the encroaching tangle of vegetation till he reached the edge of the terrace, where it dropped away into the forested hillside below. He peered and poked about in the starlight, then seeing what appeared to be a heap of brush-wood and old poppy stems at the foot of the slope whispered: 'This'll do.' He led them down. 'We'll lie up here till daylight. Peter – give me a hand unloading this mule.'

'We're too near the village!' Meg spoke with great effort. 'They'll find us in the morning.'

'We'll skip at first light. All right, Peter? Hup!' Jason heard the saddle creak and the soft thumps of sacks being swung down. 'We won't off-saddle, but I'll slacken these girths.' The mule stood unmoving and Bain swore under his breath. 'Those Haus were working this beast with slack girths; it'd have been galled to bits in another day.' Brass clinked and he grunted: 'That's it.' He tethered the mule a yard or two away.

'We've got about seven hours.'

'What then?' asked Meg.

'God knows.' Stiffly he sat down and began to fumble at his shoelaces. Suddenly he sounded very tired.

# 7
# HUNGER

JASON woke to daylight in his eyes and a hand over his mouth. 'Shhh, boy, don't make a sound!' Bain was whispering into his ear. 'We've all overslept.'

He was awake at once, stiff and aching but tensed and ready to run. They still lay in shadow, but above him the edge of the terrace was in clear sunlight. From it he heard a steady, rhythmical clunking, but whatever was making the noise was in the field itself and out of sight.

'I'll have a look.' Bain crawled up the bank of loose earth and inched his head over the top. He lay there a long moment then eased himself back down again. 'Two Lesu women hoeing the far side,' he reported. 'We're lucky – they've no dogs with them.'

'Would they help us?'

Bain shook his head. 'No, Jason. We're the foreigners. Come on, let's get out of this.' He gestured to Lacey. 'Give me a hand with the mule, will you Peter?' then stopped as he saw him crouched on the ground, Meg with him. 'He's bad again. Here, Jason, you help me.' Bain went across to the mule, clicking his tongue gently. 'Whoa there, girl, steady.' He heaved the girth strap tight and buckled it. 'Grab a sack. Manage?'

'Yes, I think so.' The bulky sack was heavy, and Jason had to struggle before he was able to get it high enough to hang on. 'Okay,' he gasped.

'Good lad. Now, I'll go ahead, you follow with the mule –' he handed Jason the leading rein – 'and the others can come behind. Pssst!' he hissed at Meg. 'Get Peter up.'

She nodded, and taking him by arm and wrist, swung him to his feet. He staggered on the loose earth and stood swaying, a sheen of sweat on his face.

'Quiet!' Bain threw an anguished glance up at the edge of the terraced field.

'Take it easy,' said Meg. 'Just lead on.'

'Listen!' They paused. Sharp and clear, the sound

of gunfire came to them, and it came both from the west and from the north. The war was closing in. 'Come on.' They plunged down into the trees.

As they moved the rhythmical clunking of the hoes grew fainter, and when at last it was nearly inaudible Bain stopped. 'Wait here,' he said. 'I think I can hear water.' He disappeared across the slope and in a few minutes came pushing back. 'There's a small stream just ahead, and I think I can see the path below it.'

'The one we came on yesterday?'

'I think so, Meg. Come on, that mule needs watering – and so do the rest of us.' In a few minutes they came to the edge of a small stream, hardly more than a tiny natural ditch. Before Jason could step aside the mule shouldered past him and began to suck up water. He smiled ruefully as he watched the stomach swell; then realized his own thirst, flopped down on his knees and, cupping his hands, drank deeply.

'Now what?' Meg was sitting by the stream rubbing Peter's wrists. 'We're out of Peter's medicine and you've lumbered us with *that* thing.' She nodded towards the mule. 'Those Haus will soon find where we went down through the field. They're probably searching now, and,' her heavy face broke into a reluctant, rather awed, grin, 'they must be like angry hornets!'

'That datura,' asked Jason. 'How long would it last?'

'Not many hours. I only put in a small amount, in case they noticed the seeds. But Angus,' she pleaded. 'Leave the mule! Let's just go!'

Bain's face set in a sullen determination. 'First I'm going to see what it's carrying. Hold her head, Jason.' He pulled open the mouth of one of the sacks, revealing the tops of two very large tins with tight-fitting lids. 'Got that dah, Meg?'

'No, I left it behind.'

Bain drew a breath of exasperation. 'How'll we lever these open?' He looked round hurriedly: 'We've got no time. I know they've got dope in there, I think it's heroin and I'm not leaving it. Now listen. You three hide upstream, among the thick stuff. I'll take the mule back a bit to where the ground's soft, go down the path and walk on as if we're heading back to that Akha village where we were locked up. Then I'll double back here, and when the Haus go past we'll –'

'We'll go back down last night's ridge?'

'That's it, Meg. It should lead us to the Kwan gorge. Quite clear? Right, then. We must be quick.'

Hurriedly they moved deeper uphill away from the path below and off-loaded the mule in a thick patch of jungle.

'I don't like it.' Meg looked mutinous. 'I don't like it a bit.'

Ignoring her Bain walked across to where Lacey sat against the sacks. 'You don't look too good, Peter; I'd better relieve you of that shotgun.' He picked it up and turned to Jason: 'Ever handled one of these things before?'

'No, I haven't.'

'All I want you to do is to carry it. Peter's pretty bad, and he might drop it. Here's the safety catch.'

Jason took the heavy weapon gingerly, keeping his hands carefully away from the trigger.

'Your business isn't to shoot, except to escape recapture. Got it?'

'Got it.' Jason felt uneasy again, and he held the weapon with an assumption of confidence he did not feel.

'Right, I'm off. Sit down and keep quiet everyone – I'll be back inside half an hour.' He led the mule back the way they had come, and in a few minutes the others heard the clop of hooves and saw Bain and mule hurrying past below.

'Now we sit and wait.' Meg and Peter sat leaning against the sacks. For long minutes there was silence, then Jason heard a peculiar sound, and he turned his head sharply. Peter Lacey was doubled up and gasping and as Jason watched in dismay Lacey jerked his legs straight out and his feet curved outwards, straining tight in their shoes, while his head strained back the other way. He was groaning and yawning.

Jason swung round to Meg: 'What's the matter? Is he having a fit?' He looked back at Lacey with horror. That handsome face was contorted repeatedly, the mouth opened wide in great yawns, and Jason wondered fearfully if he was going to dislocate his jaw. What scared him most was the noise: any Hau who came along the path now would be bound to hear this inarticulate crying. 'What shall we do?' he asked Meg helplessly. She was gripping Lacey by the arms, trying to stop him jerking about, and Jason put down the shotgun and ran to help her. He seized one arm. The muscles were taut, and hard as a board. Meg looked desperate: 'I think I can fix it – but Jason, you go off, I want you to go back along the slope and give me warning if those Hau appear.'

'All right.' He started to run off through the trees

then remembered: he'd left the shotgun on the ground. He ran back and picked it up, keeping the muzzle pointed well away from his feet. He started to run, then slowed to a walk; if he tripped that thing might go off. He could still hear Lacey's inarticulate cries; they'd carry a long way through the trees – suppose the village people heard; would they come and see? Then what should they do, would he have to fight them? He stopped where he could see the path, and from behind came a series of animal-like howls and Jason shrank against a tree; he felt like covering his ears.

Suddenly, like a radio being switched off, the howls stopped. Jason listened, but there were no more. Somehow or other Meg had quietened Lacey's ravings. He looked down at the shotgun: the hand clenching it was white to the knuckles. He relaxed his grip and watched the blood come slowly back. He wondered how Bain was getting on – then his heart jumped and he flattened himself against the tree.

Moving at a rapid padding walk a single Hau appeared on the path below. He stooped, examined something, and padded on again. Jason clutched the shotgun. Even at this range he recognized the man; it was the one with the little black moustache, the man who had clubbed him in the kidneys. Suddenly the shotgun no longer seemed an awkward and dangerous encumbrance. Then a second man came into view and Jason felt his heart jump again, for this was the leader, the strange pale-skinned man, and he too was walking fast, pistol in hand. Close behind him came a third, then a fourth and fifth – but no sign of a sixth man.

Jason stood jammed against the tree while the Haus hurried along below him. The men looked weary, their sweaty faces blotchy from the effects of the drug, and he heard the rasp of breath above the thud of their feet on the beaten earth of the path. He did not dare move to warn Meg, and he prayed Peter wouldn't groan or cry out. He waited. Five Haus had passed; presumably the sixth must be following well behind, a kind of Tail-end Charlie. Half a minute, then a whole minute ticked by, still there was no sign of the sixth man, and Jason left his sheltering tree and hurried back to the others.

Peter still lay stretched out, but not with the bow-like tension of a few minutes before, and Meg looked at Jason with relief. 'I managed to help him.' Peter took a deep breath, opened his eyes and lay gazing upwards, and she smiled faintly: 'It's all right for a bit.' She looked harder at Jason. 'You've seen something.'

He nodded. He was still shaken, and when he did speak it was in jerky phrases: 'The Haus.' He stood the shotgun gingerly against a tree. 'They came past just as you got him quiet.'

Her eyes did not leave his face. He went on: 'They were moving pretty fast, faster than Angus.'

'He's got that gun.'

'He may not hear them behind him.' A wild idea formed in his mind. 'I'd better go after them. Perhaps I can warn him.'

'No, you mustn't do that. We'll just wait here. He had a good start, and anyway he wasn't going too far.' Her matter-of-fact approach reassured Jason – and then he remembered something that had worried him. 'There were only five Haus,' he said. 'Perhaps there's one waiting, covering the way back to the ridge.'

'Only five? Are you sure?'

'Certain.' Jason again felt that twinge of terror at the sight of those swiftly-moving men in their ragged clothes. 'There was Moustache first, then that leader, the pale-faced man; then close together three more – and no one after that.'

'In that case –' she shrugged. 'One's had a little too much datura.'

'Would it kill him?'

'No. He'd either be very sick indeed, or he'd go out of his mind for a few hours. They'd have just left him. Well, that's one less to worry about.'

Just then Peter sat up. To Jason's astonishment he looked completely normal – his yellowish sheen replaced by a normal, healthy colour; his pale blue eyes again clear and his speech articulate.

'Hullo, Jason.' He gave a faint smile. 'I gather I had an attack.'

'You weren't too good.' Jason tried to speak re-assuringly, but he felt awkward and uneasy. That terrifying fit, those animal howls, the cramp that bent the body outwards like a bow – what strange malady caused that?

Peter Lacey spoke again and Jason's morbid fancies lifted; once again, even in his stained and dirty clothes, he seemed the elegant figure that Jason had first seen engrossed in the detail of an inscription in the ruins of Nakhon Wat. 'It seems that we nearly had company!'

Meg's brow cleared. 'Better, Pete?' She put a hand

on his shoulder and he gave it a casual squeeze. 'M'm. How did you manage?'

She did not answer directly, simply saying: 'We should be able to keep you going long enough till we all get out of this.' His eyebrows lifted but she said – with relief, it seemed to Jason – 'Here's Angus.'

Man and mule came walking quickly through the trees towards them, every few yards Angus looking back over his shoulder. 'Did you see them?'

'Jason saw them,' said Meg. 'He was up on the spur there.'

Angus turned to him. 'How many did you see, Jason?'

'Five.'

'Same here. One may be sick, but we must be careful.'

'They were going at a good lick when they passed below us here.' Jason gave a worried smile. 'I thought they'd catch you up.'

'I'll tell you something,' said Angus. 'That's a good mule we've got.' He patted her neck. 'She kept turning her ears back, so I reckoned at last – and nearly too late – that there was something following us. She didn't whinny, so I knew it wasn't another animal, and I put two and two together and it added up to half a dozen Haus. Anyway, I got off the track at the very first spot where the ground began hardening up, and hid. Sure enough, in three to four minutes they passed. Now we'd better move.' He led the mule towards the two sacks on the ground. 'Jason, give a hand here, will you?' He bent to lift one of the sacks, but paused, 'Hullo!'

'What's the trouble?' Meg's eyes were fixed on him. 'Something wrong?'

'No, nothing wrong.' He pulled open one of the sacks. 'I tried the wrong tin this morning – this one's been opened already!' He spoke with mounting excitement. 'Of course – the Haus must have checked on what they were taking, probably when we were all asleep yesterday morning!' He looked carefully at the circular lid. 'See these scratches? They took a knife blade or something to it. I'll get it off.'

'We'll have to hurry.' Jason spoke nervously. 'Suppose those Haus turn back!'

'We'll soon find out if this is worth taking.' Bain fumbled with the lid. 'It's not on straight. Aha!' He lifted it off, and very gently pulled out from the tin a flat packet of pure white crystalline powder. 'Here you are, Jason! Do you remember what I told you?' Across the packet was emblazoned, in rather blotchy blue ink, a device of a globe with a tiger springing across it. 'Globe and Tiger,' he said calmly, striving to keep the triumph from his voice.

Meg was watching him, a wary expression on her face. 'Well?'

'It's heroin. We *must* take it.'

'Take just one packet!' suggested Jason. 'That would prove you found it!'

'I could have carried it in with me. No.' He shook his head. 'For absolute proof I need all of this.'

'Sure you don't just need it for a newspaper story?' sneered Meg.

He gave her a hard look. 'I do not – and you know as well as I do that every kilo of heroin reaching the

West causes a precisely calculated number of murders, overdose deaths, robberies and muggings as well as broken lives. No.' Again he shook his head. 'Now we've got this I'm going to take it out and I'm going to show just how much has been coming through. We'll load up. Jason?'

'Right.' Together they swung up the sacks.

'Let's hope we make it!' Meg turned away, apparently indifferent.

Peter asked: 'Where now – back up to the east ridge?'

'Yes. Will you take the shotgun again?' Bain handed him the gun, saw that the mule-load was properly hooked on and gave the rein to Jason. 'Once on that track it should be downhill all the way.' He set off and Jason followed, almost light-headedly bubbling with relief. The thought of the Haus chasing along in the wrong direction appealed to him and he called forward to Bain: 'You must have laughed to see them go past!'

'Not really.' Angus looked back at Jason ironically, then softened his tone. 'There's one thing that might interest you, though, as an old Far East hand!'

'What was that?' Jason only half-listened: his mind was on their return arrival back in Thailand – could they make it by tomorrow?

'You remember how we'd been puzzled about the leader – how he sat apart, how his behaviour seemed different?'

'Yes?'

'I got a good look at him from very close.' Bain gave a faintly embarrassed laugh. 'If it weren't quite ludi-

crous I'd have said without hesitation that he was
Japanese.' He lifted a hand towards Meg and Peter.
'We'll move carefully now up to the poppy fields. Keep
a good fifty yards behind and watch for my signals. All
right, Jason?'

'All right.' He answered mechanically, his balloon of
euphoria pricked by that one barbed word 'Japanese'.
There *was* one Japanese unaccounted for, though far
to the south. Again Jason saw that pale face glimpsed
momentarily behind the cockpit glass of the hijacked
aircraft. Yasuno had never been found. Could *this*
Japanese be the missing hijacker? Then Jason gasped to
himself: suppose Yasuno had always meant to lead his
gang, equipped with modern weapons bought with the
proceeds from the hijack, up into the Golden Triangle!
A group of totally ruthless Japanese terrorists would
very quickly have seized themselves a fat share of this
golden harvest, and the good-natured Shans could not
have stopped them. But the hijack had failed, leaving
Yasuno to struggle up here on his own and fall in with
a rag-tag band of Haus – and it had failed because of
Jason. If it indeed *were* Yasuno, and if the terrorist ever
found out about him . . . He licked his dry lips. If he
had identified Yasuno earlier he might well have given
himself away by his own fear. Yasuno would have
smelt him out. It was just as well that they were
travelling in different directions; still, he wouldn't
feel really safe until he had crossed the river back into
Thailand. All that mattered now was to get away.

As they climbed they heard the faint thud, thud of
mattocks and the occasional clink of a stone. Sunlight
showed through the trees and Bain gestured back for

silence. They were moving on very slowly when there was a whinny from ahead, the snorting whinny of a mule. Jason felt his own mule's head go up, saw the teeth drawn back – and in desperation seized the animal by its nostrils. It swung its head but remained silent.

Angus Bain came hurrying back, signalling to the other three. 'Did you hear that? I think there's something wrong. Village people can't usually afford mules – but there's one up there. Jason, you're light on your feet. Go up very carefully and have a good look. I'll hold the mule.'

Jason climbed the slope, coming out by the heap of brushwood where they had slept. Very slowly he crawled up to the top of the terrace and peeped through the fringe of grass and weeds.

Groups of men were busy with long-handled mattocks, but they were not village men, nor were they digging for cultivation. They were uniformed and armed, and they were digging weapon pits. Propped on their bipods and covering the open terraces in front were light machine-guns. Jason stared at the troops, and stared again, for they were Chinese.

His immediate emotion was not fright, but an intense curiosity. What on earth were Chinese troops doing here? Although they were too close for comfort – the nearest group little more than sixty yards away – he felt a measure of confidence. He was well enough hidden, and he knew he could bolt down into the concealing forest if one of them made so much as a move towards him. He lay there studying them. They were Chinese, all right; they had the regular features, rather hollow cheeks and sallow, almost parchment-coloured complexions of men from the North. Their clothing, which was in good condition, seemed standard for any army in Asia – olive-green trousers and shirt, rubber-soled canvas boots, webbing belts with ammunition pouches and aluminium water-bottles, and cloth caps with short, stitched peaks. Their weapons, too, looked new, the blueing on the barrels gleamed and the woodwork was dark and well-cared for. But Chinese! There was some other characteristic about them, something he felt he should identify, but which eluded him.

But he had seen enough. He started to inch his way back down the slope and when he had reached the bottom of the loose earth he ducked into the trees and ran towards the three others.

'All right?' asked Bain. 'I thought we'd lost you!' Then he saw Jason's face and said sharply: 'What did you see?'

Jason took a deep breath. Even now he wondered if he had been right! Trying to make his voice natural and matter-of-fact he said: 'Chinese soldiers, digging trenches.'

Bain blinked, Meg gave him a swift, sideways glance and Peter Lacey raised his eyebrows and smiled: 'You mean Shans.'

'Ah,' said Meg, also looking pleased. 'Of course – Shans.'

'No, not Shans,' insisted Jason. 'These men were all in uniform, and had machine-guns!' He cast a worried look back up towards the terrace edge, out of sight through the trees but still he could hear the thud-clink of digging.

'Shans have these things too, Jason,' said Meg but Bain, still watching Jason, said: 'I think he knows a Chinese soldier when he sees one.'

'They were Chinese, all right,' said Jason gratefully, 'but not South Chinese. These are from the North – they're much taller. One thing,' he remembered now what it was that had eluded him. 'They're mostly quite old!'

'Of course.' Angus Bain turned quickly to the others. 'They must be KMT – Kuo Min Tang, survivors from the Nationalist forces. They've been roaming the Burmese border area for twenty years – and *they're* in the opium trade as well. Now do you believe him?'

'If that's so,' said Peter Lacey doubtfully, 'what are they doing up on that ridge?'

'Listen.' A drift of wind carried to them the sound of gunfire. 'The Burmese are cutting through to the north, and the KMT may be getting out of their way. I'll see how far they've got beyond the village. You come along behind, Jason; you can warn the others if I get caught.'

They crept up and circled till they reached the edge of the trees near the village itself. It resembled the Akha village in layout – a gateway, with its cluster of offerings, an open space and then houses, each on its own little terrace. The ridge path was higher up, and groups of men were passing along it at intervals.

'So much for *that* way down.' Bain's face was grim.

'Look over there!' Jason was staring at something among the first houses. 'The KMT have got hold of someone!' Several Chinese soldiers were standing round a man seated on the ground, knees drawn up and hands fastened beneath them. He was bare-headed, but his ragged clothing was black. 'It's that last Hau!' hissed Jason. 'They must have caught him trying to cross the ridge!'

'They're asking him questions, by the look of it.'

'Do you think he'll talk?'

Bain grimaced. 'Does he want to live? I'm afraid that by now the KMT know that not far away there's a million dollars' worth of heroin being led about on a mule by four rather part-worn Europeans.'

'What will they do?'

'Depends on how hard the Burmese are pressing them. But if they've got a little time, Jason, they're going to come looking for us. Come on, it's time we moved.'

'A near thing earlier while you were away, with the mule,' said Jason as they walked down. 'Peter was very bad for a bit, and making a terrible noise. If he hadn't stopped the Haus would have heard for sure.'

'Oh?' Bain stopped. 'Just what sort of noise?'

'Well, it was groaning, really, but he was all bent – like a bow, as if he had a fearful cramp.' Jason made a face. 'I've never seen anything like it. Meg fixed it, though – she sent me off to watch and suddenly he stopped.'

'I see,' said Bain very thoughtfully. 'It was lucky he stopped so suddenly.' He walked on slowly, frowning to himself, then quickened his pace again, as he saw the other two ahead.

'We thought you'd been captured,' said Meg briskly as Jason and Bain returned. 'Well, were they Shans?'

'Not on your life. Jason was absolutely right. They're

KMT, there are scores of them, more are moving down, and –' he paused a moment to let the import of his words sink in – 'they've captured that last Hau and it looks as if he's talking his head off.'

During this recital Peter Lacey's handsome face had been getting steadily gloomier. 'So there may now be two lots after us.'

'Two?'

'Yes. The Haus and now the KMT!'

'That makes three,' said Bain evenly. 'You've forgotten the Shans.'

'Oh, of course,' agreed Peter. 'The Shans too.'

'Dragon's teeth,' Meg commented drily. Jason frowned: the allusion was one he should have known well – then he remembered the story of that first Jason, as one of his tasks towards finding the Golden Fleece, ploughing a field with two enchanted bulls and sowing it with the teeth of a dragon, and said: 'Armed men sprang from the very earth all round!'

'Exactly,' said Meg. 'And what are we going to do about it?'

'There are KMT on the east ridge, Shans and maybe Haus on the west ridge, and some sort of battle further north – which is the wrong way anyway. That leaves one way out.' Bain nodded downhill. 'About two thousand feet straight down that slope. It's bound to come out at the gorge.'

'Looks rough.' Meg shrugged. 'At least we can try.'

With Bain once again leading they set off downhill.

Late morning found them struggling across a steepening, crumbling slope, close to exhaustion and wondering which way to move. They communicated by signals, for the stream was now a torrent whose roar drowned all else but shouts. Jason's main worry was the mule. He himself was progressing in scrambling rushes, trying to gauge with every few steps whether the earth would crumble away beneath his feet. Continually he wondered why the mule, its load bumping against the slope, had not vanished kicking into the depths on any one of a dozen occasions – but she always seemed to recover and struggle on. He spoke to her a lot, as much for his own morale as hers; he christened her Jenny, which seemed an appropriate name somehow. She hadn't been fed properly for days, he knew: 'We're just beasts of burden, Jenny!' he panted, in between scrambling rushes to the next foothold, 'beasts of burden!'

At last the slope steepened into very nearly a sheer precipice, over which the torrent vanished. Clinging to a tree Bain turned and shouted above the roar of the falls: 'We'll have to go back up again!'

'Can't we get round the side?' Meg's voice was half lost in the noise and she clambered forward to him. 'What about getting round?' she shouted again.

'All too steep!' He waved his hand from side to side in a gesture of hopelessness. 'If one of us slips . . .'

Wearily they turned back and began to struggle uphill again. Slowly and painfully they climbed, and at last, by mid-afternoon, they were back more or less where they had started by the path and the stream.

Jason and Bain unloaded the mule. She stood with drooping head, and showed little improvement even after Jason had watered her at the stream. 'She needs

fodder,' said Bain. He rubbed the heavy black stubble
on his jaw. 'I don't think she'll go much farther without
some.' He smiled without any humour at all. 'That
goes for all of us.'

'I don't think Peter can do much more,' Meg spoke
in a low voice.

'That settles it,' said Bain. 'There's only one place
where there's food, and that's the village. We'll have to
get it from there.'

# 8

# THE DREAM

'THAT village is full of soldiers – you said so yourself!'
Meg stared at Bain. 'It would be impossible to raid it
for food!'

'I think there *is* a way of getting food, though it'll be
risky.' He turned to Jason. 'Do you remember that
open space in front of the village?' At Jason's nod he

went on: 'There was the usual gateway, but this side of it there were some small posts stuck in the ground, with pots and dishes beside them.'

'Yes, it was something like that.' Jason remembered vaguely; he'd been too concerned with the KMT troops to pay much attention to these other details.

'These villagers are animists, like all these hill people. I think that's where they put out their daily offerings to the spirits – offerings of food.'

'You mean –' Jason stopped. The thought of touching a religious offering repelled him, yet his instinct struggled with the thought of food – *any* food. 'I don't like it,' he muttered, faintly conscious that he must be appearing as a superstitious fool.

Bain nodded in understanding. 'I'd thought of that, too, Jason, and I was put off by the idea just as you are – till I remembered something.' He smiled. 'We wouldn't be depriving the spirits of their offering. After a decent interval the villagers take it back and eat it themselves.'

'Oh.' Jason was rather nonplussed. That seemed to make it rather less sacrilegious.

'In fact,' said Bain rather primly, 'we may even convince them that the spirits have at last accepted their offerings!'

For a moment Meg's heavy, sombre expression lightened into a smile and Jason felt more cheerful. 'All right,' he said. 'But we'll have to be careful!'

'Let's just hope the KMT think we're locals if they spot us. Coming?'

'Yes.' Jason handed the reins to Meg and followed him up the slope towards the village.

The open space before the ancestral gateway to the village was empty, but beyond it Chinese soldiers, some shirtless, moved about between the houses, where the smoke of half a dozen small cooking fires rose.

From the ridge beyond came the occasional sound of a voice, and once or twice Jason, from his hiding place at the edge of the trees, caught a glimpse of a rifle over an olive-green shoulder, a peaked cloth cap bobbing along or a sallow face glancing round. There was still movement along the path, though by small groups of seldom more than two or three men at a time, with long gaps in between. Jason and Bain, however, fixed their attention on the shrine – a few axe-dressed planks set upright in the ground, one or two of them ornamented with strips of cloth, before them chinaware dishes and a heap of pale buff objects that he could not identify. Earlier Jason had looked on the task as hopeless; now, however, he felt a first lift of hope, for the shrine was not right out in the open but shaded by a grove of low trees rather to one side.

Jason had as yet no idea how Bain intended that they should approach the grove, and he whispered nervously: 'Perhaps if we move round a bit . . .'

'All right.' They stepped back from the edge of the trees and began to try to find their way round, but once away from the immediate area of the village, where grazing animals had kept the confines more or less clear, a tangle of secondary growth had sprung up, springy and impenetrable. Defeated, the two of them retreated back among the taller trees.

Bain wiped sweat from his face and Jason scratched

at his neck; dust from the short tangle had settled inside his shirt, making him itch and sniff.

Crouched at the edge of the trees once more, Bain explained his plan: 'The simplest thing is for me to walk across, collect what I can and walk back again.' Jason looked at him, startled, and Bain went on: 'The simplest way is often the best. I'll leave you the Sten. If someone tries to grab me, open up in their general direction, but not to hit anyone. Got it?' He unslung the Sten gun and laid it beside Jason. 'It's loaded and cocked. Just turn down this steel cocking handle here and you can blaze away. Think you can manage?'

Jason looked at the weapon with growing unease. He knew how to handle a rifle, but this ancient machine-gun with its lethal magazineful of ammunition . . . And suppose he fired and hit Bain?

Bain understood his hesitation at once. 'Perhaps you might just get the wrong man.' He smiled faintly. 'Never mind the shooting, then – but be ready to run for it, will you?'

Jason found his voice. 'You do the covering. *I'll* go.'

'No –'

'I mean it,' insisted Jason. 'We might have a chance then.'

'Very well. One thing – try and keep some of those small trees between you and the village as you move.' Then, 'Damn!' He struck his thigh in exasperation. 'I should have brought something to carry the food in. We can't go back loaded with plates like a couple of waiters!'

At the thought Jason gave an uneasy grin, then said,

'I'm not muleman for nothing.' He unslung from his shoulder the mule's empty feed-bag, and Bain breathed a quick sigh of relief.

The two stood upright behind a big tree, peering out. One or two Chinese soldiers moved about, there was a call from the ridge and an answering call from somewhere in the terraced poppy fields. Bain tucked the Sten gun into the crook of his arm, and with a last look round said: 'Ready, Jason lad?'

'Ready.'

'If you hear me shout or open fire, make off downhill for the others, get them moving and keep going. I'll catch you up later. Got it?'

'Got it.'

'Don't walk too fast. Off you go.'

Jason stepped out from behind the tree and began walking at an angle across the open space towards the grove. He deliberately kept himself from looking towards the group of houses on the far side, just in case his eye or the movement of his head caught the eye of some villager or Chinese soldier. He counted his paces: seven, eight, nine . . . He strode on steadily, realized he was getting faster and faster and made himself slow down. Eighteen, nineteen, twenty . . . He lost count. Was it twenty? Had he missed one? The grove was close now, and he turned his eyes momentarily towards the village, but all seemed quiet.

Suddenly he was within the shade of the small trees – still in full view of the village but somehow feeling rather more protected – and there was the shrine. He hesitated. Hunger made him light-headed, and he felt a twinge of superstitious fear. He knelt, and just as he did so a Chinese soldier appeared at the entrance to the village. Jason, still on his knees in the shade, kept very still. A moment or two later he stole a glance. The soldier was lighting a cigarette, and after taking one or two puffs wandered back among the houses. Jason's hands trembled. He could hardly believe his good fortune. The shadow thrown by the small trees, his own position – kneeling, as if in prayer, and his tattered, dirty clothes – had probably induced the Chinese to think him one of the villagers, if indeed, he had noticed him at all.

Quickly Jason emptied the contents of the bowls into the feed-bag – half a dozen bowls of boiled rice, cold now and covered with insects; some salt, coarse and greyish; what looked like string beans but might have been chillies, and those buff objects. His heart leapt: they were corn-cobs, boiled and wrapped in their original outer leaves. In spite of his haste and his fear the sight and smell of the cold food made his mouth water, and it was all he could do to resist cramming a handful of rice into his mouth as he worked, but he fought off the temptation, and at last, all bowls and dishes successfully emptied, he stood up. His feelings of apprehension and remorse had vanished, replaced by one of confidence – almost as if the spirits of the forest approved. He slung the bag from his shoulder and walked casually back towards the trees. He knew now that no one would call to him or hurry to seize him, and he was smiling when he stepped into the shade. A tense Bain stared at him: 'You're a cool one! Did you not see that fellow who came out?' He let out a long breath. 'He looked straight at you. I really thought we were for it!'

'Look at this!' Jason opened the bag and Bain's eyes gleamed. 'Come on.' He slapped Jason on the shoulder and together they melted away among the trees.

Meg and Peter were deep in talk when the two reached them, and it was not until Bain said quietly: 'Done it!' that they looked up.

Jason was taken aback at the suspicion on the two faces, and Meg spoke sharply: 'We didn't hear you come!'

Bain ignored her hostile tone. 'We've brought you a nice surprise,' he said in a bantering voice – though Jason thought he detected an edge in it. 'We've brought the food.'

At Meg's startled expression he smiled: 'You didn't think we'd manage, did you now?' He knelt and opened the feed-bag. 'Come on, we'll eat and then we'll put some distance between us and the KMT.' He drew out a boiled corn-cob and Peter smiled eagerly, 'Indian corn! You couldn't have done better!'

'Ah-ah,' admonished Bain. 'Those are for the mule, aren't they, Jason?'

'Indeed they are!' Jason felt a surge of relief; he'd felt guilty about fodder for the mule, he'd never thought of the corn-cobs! 'I'll take them to her now.' He gathered up the yellow cobs and was walking towards Jenny when a thought struck him and he turned back, feeling rather a fool. 'How does a mule eat corn-cobs?'

The sudden silence was broken by a burst of laughter, till Bain hissed a warning: 'The KMT are just up the hill!' To Jason he said, 'Put them down in front of her and see that the bit is out of her mouth. She'll do the rest! Now, let's eat ourselves, quick, and then we can get out of here.'

Meg took the nose-bag, dived her hand into it and drew out a handful of cold rice. All eyes were on it. 'Jason first.' He demurred but she said, 'No backchat, boy – hands out!' Obediently he held out both hands and she dumped the rice into it. He waited till she had given a handful each to Bain and Peter, and had taken a handful herself – then all ate, with no pretence at delicacy. In three or four gulps the rice was gone, and they looked up expectantly for more. 'Next round!' she called, again there was a handful each and in his Jason found a lump of raw salt. He took it out of his mouth with a grimace, and Bain asked him if the rice were not to his taste. 'Lump of salt,' he replied.

'Try it on the mule.' At Jason's wry look Bain repeated, 'Try it on the mule – but be careful, give it her in your open palm, or she'll have your hand as well.'

Sure enough, at the smell of it Jenny snatched at his hand, the lump of salt vanished and he heard her champing and then licking the insides of her teeth. Bain smiled at his surprise. 'She's been marched about with a heavy load for days, and she's lost nearly all her body salt in sweat. We've had a little, but she needs a lot.' He looked around. 'Everyone finished? We'd better move.' He nodded to Jason, and without a word they moved across to the mule, saddled her up and loaded on the sacks. It was done without conscious thought, and as Jason ran a finger along the edge of the girth to check its tightness he reflected that the pattern had not taken long to root itself in him – saddle up, load up, check girths and harness, march . . . He took the leading rein and looked back at the others. All were worn and dirty, but what struck him was how they were all beginning to look part of the forest. The men's stubbly beards replaced the normal shine of shaven cheeks; hair, clinging close to the head, was roughly parted to let the eyes see; clothes were moulded to the shape of the body, and with the stains of opium and leaf mould and earth were blending into the very colours of the forest itself. They had eaten the food set out for the spirits of the forest, so perhaps those same spirits would protect them. He felt a rush of confidence.

'And where, may I ask, are we going?' Peter Lacey, still with a kind of raffish elegance about him, raised an eyebrow in delicate inquiry.

'There's only one way left,' replied Bain. 'Back the way we first came. We'll just have to hope the Haus give up and go home when they don't find us, and that the Shans are being too bothered by the Burmese Army to bother about us.'

'That sounds eminently sensible.' Lacey did not disguise his relief.

'I'll go well ahead,' said Bain. 'Meg, you come next and keep a sharp eye on me. If I wave my hand downwards' – he demonstrated – 'get off the path and hide, and don't move till I wave you forward again. There's a lot of movement about.' He turned his head west, in the direction they were heading. Almost imperceptibly the distant crepitation they had heard earlier drifted to them on the wind, a spasmodic vibration, interrupted by sharp thuds. 'The evening battle!' Then he said: 'Give me at least fifty yards. When you can, let me get ahead farther than that – just so long as you keep me in sight.' He unslung the Sten. 'If you hear any of this, clear off at once.'

'What about you?' Meg asked him.

'I'll get away as best I can. Everyone all right? You manage, Peter?'

Lacey nodded. 'I'm all right today.' He slung the shotgun from his shoulder.

Jason studied him from behind the mule. It was curious how Lacey had seemed so bad this morning and yet had recovered so quickly. And why had he not had a recurrence of that seizure or fit or whatever it was?

With a last look round Bain vanished in the direction of the path, and then Meg strode off, stocky and determined; hardly a wood-nymph, Jason thought with an inward smile – but it was perhaps all the better for them that she was her own forceful self.

'I'll go next, Jason.' Peter followed her down, Jason waited till he was several yards ahead then lifted the leading rein. 'Come, Jenny.' They had begun the long journey home.

After the steep, crumbly forest slopes, walking on the narrow beaten path was almost effortless. To Jason it seemed that they were no more than sauntering along, till he remembered that ahead of them Bain would be moving very carefully indeed, pausing frequently to try and see ahead, hurrying along the straighter sections and going very slowly where the path wound among trees. More than once Peter Lacey stopped, and Jason stopped too, his left hand lifting the rein in an

instinctive message to the mule – but each time, after a
pause, Lacey moved on again. These pauses became
routine, with each one Jason losing a little of that quick
race in the blood that tensed his muscles – till Peter
Lacey stopped, swung round, his face contorted into
fierce warning, and with a sweep of his hand signalled
'Hide!'

Jason turned to plunge downward from the path –
then saw that the patchy undergrowth between the
trees would conceal a man lying down but not a mule
standing up. With Jenny trotting behind him he ran
back along the path, looking desperately to right and
left. Above the path, now – that might just do the trick!
He was panting, and the noise of the hooves on the
hard earth sounded terribly loud, but he rounded a
corner, looked around frantically and spotted a little
thicket of saplings and bushes between the bigger trees
uphill. Lengthening the leading rein to give the mule
room to scramble up behind him he climbed hastily,
led Jenny up and round behind the saplings and sat
himself on the ground by her forelegs, holding her
bridle just below the bit. The cover was not complete,
but it was the best he could do.

The path below jinked into the hillside and back out
in a V, and Jason felt instinctively that men following
the path would tend to look forward across the V, in the
direction they were going, rather than turn to examine
the slopes behind them.

He tried to see what he could through the trees and
undergrowth above the path, but there was a hump of
hillside in the way. As well, the late evening sun was
flashing its rays through between the branches and

into his eyes, so he just sat waiting, holding the bridle and carefully stroking the mule's muzzle. Occasionally she shifted the weight on her feet; standing unevenly on the slope seemed to bother her, and once or twice she swished her tail and stamped. Jason looked desperately at those powerful hooves. One or two of those stamps when someone was passing would give him away as quickly as if he were to shout aloud. He was wondering exactly how to keep her still when his attention was forcibly distracted. Soundless in rubber-soled boots a Chinese soldier walked round the corner.

Jason froze. He was looking down at a considerable angle, and he could only see the lower half of the man's face, but he was certainly Chinese. Jason now realized that he was rather too close to the path for comfort; the man was not much more than twenty feet below him, perhaps not that – so close, in fact, that Jason saw the long, carefully tended hairs of the mole on his cheek. But the Chinese was looking, not up at the saplings but towards the slope on the far side of the V, and the M-16 carbine tucked under his arm also swung up towards it. He walked on steadily, but just before he turned the far corner he looked back. Jason's heart nearly stopped beating – but the gaze was to see whether he was still being followed, and round the corner came a second soldier.

Once again the pattern was repeated – the head turning up to examine the slope ahead, and at the corner a glance back. Half a dozen men in single file then followed the path round, plodded on and vanished. One or two looked about them, but only the last man looked back – and that made Jason wary. Stiff and

uncomfortable, he resisted the temptation to stand up
and ease his cramped legs and, in particular, to remove
from himself what felt like a set of sharp and thorny
twigs. He'd give it just a minute, he decided; somehow
the air didn't seem quite clear. He stayed crouched,
automatically stroking at Jenny's muzzle while the
mule stood patiently, unmoving except for an occasional
quick swish of the tail. Jason was at last going to stand
and drop down to the path when, again with hardly a
sound, two more soldiers walked round the corner.
They too looked up and forward, but neither made any
attempt to glance behind as they turned the far corner
and disappeared.

Jason knew they must be the last. He stood up stiffly,
plucked the twigs from the seat of his thin trousers
and paused a moment to scratch the mule's ears.
'Good girl,' he whispered, scratching busily and very
gratefully. 'Good girl!' With a final clap on the
shoulder he slithered down the slope and on to the
path. 'Come on.'

Anxious faces greeted him. 'You hid the mule,
then?' Bain ran towards him. 'We thought they'd be
bound to get you!'

'No.' Jason patted Jenny's neck. 'She kept very
quiet. But do you think they were looking for us?'

'Oh, certainly – they were looking for us, all right.
They had no other reason to go patrolling out towards
that west ridge, which they must know is Shan territory. No,' he repeated, 'there's no doubt they were
after us, and they'll try again in the morning. They're
bound to find hoofprints and mule droppings here and
there. There's one good thing, though.'

'What's that?'

'They've probably frightened off any of those Haus who were hanging about. That bunch wouldn't risk being picked up by the KMT. They'll have certainly gone home – if they haven't already.'

Not Yasuno, said Jason, not that fanatic, but he said it to himself.

'We'll get on.' Bain looked towards the setting sun. 'We might manage a mile or two before it's quite dark.' He turned to walk on, then glanced worriedly at Peter Lacey. 'Are you all right? I thought I saw you favouring your right arm?'

Lacey flinched, then forced a smile. 'I may have strained it a bit during that climb this morning.'

'Well, don't forget to let us know if we can do anything.'

They walked steadily in the fading light, and at last Bain said, 'Here.' He led off downhill. 'Nearly left it too late,' he grunted. They moved down through the trees in a deep shade already darkening into gloom, and at the first patch of near-level ground he stopped. 'We're well away from the path. This'll just have to do.'

While Meg and Peter sank down and examined their feet he and Jason unloaded the mule, unbuckled the girth and swung off the saddle, and Jason changed bridle for headstall – just as if he'd been doing it all his life.

'No galls,' said Bain, running a hand over her withers. 'Give her back a rub, Jason; she's very sweaty and we've no horse-blanket for her, but it'll help the circulation. Eh, lass –' he rubbed her muzzle and scratched her ears. 'We'll make it yet – and when we do you'll have a feed of oats you'll long remember. I could do with a bowl of oatmeal myself,' he added turning away. 'Keep clear of those feet after dark, Jason; you don't want to get trodden on, even by mistake.'

'All right.' Jason moved away a few yards, and sat on the ground. His shirt was soaked round his waist where he had sweated, and he cursed himself wearily for not having let it flap out to dry as they were walking. The trouble was, he realized, he had too much on his mind: gnawing hunger struggling for first place over gnawing worry.

Jason scraped a little form for himself and huddled up in it. In the stillness he heard gunfire. Someone was fighting, and not too far away; there were indeed armed men all around. He remembered Meg's remark when they first saw the KMT troops: 'Dragon's teeth, Jason!' He now remembered exactly where that came from: it was from the story of the Argonauts, and he heard his father's voice telling him how that first Jason, as a task towards securing the Golden Fleece, had sown a field with dragon's teeth, how armed men had sprung up from the ground and how Meg – no, stupid, not Meg, it was Medea – had told Jason how to escape them.

Through the branches he saw the glitter of stars. The ground was dry here, it was still the dry season . . .

It was after the first hours of heavy, almost drugged sleep, yet just before the cold woke him that he had his dream. It was short, stark and vivid. He was alone with the sack-loads of heroin on a high, bare ridge.

Although it was night he was able to see Shans, Chinese and Haus and – even in his dream he was puzzled – someone whom he could not identify calling Jason in accented English. They were all round him, all enemies, reaching out for the heroin – but larger than them all loomed a dragon, scales, pointed tail and all, but with Yasuno's head. It reached out – but whether for the heroin or for himself he could not tell. 'Dragon's teeth, Jason.' It was Meg – no, Medea . . . 'Jason!' He heard her voice again: 'Jason.'

He sat up with a start, shivering violently. It was pitch dark and very cold. He felt frightened, still seeing Yasuno's face, the eyes fixed upon – Jason or heroin? But there it was again: 'Jason!'

'Hullo,' he gasped, hoping that whoever it was wouldn't notice the slight quaver in his voice. His teeth began to chatter, and he groaned with the cold. How long until morning and the sun?

'Jason?' Meg was calling softly. 'Are you awake, Jason?'

'Yes.' He forced out the word through his chattering teeth. 'What time is it?'

'The Haus took my watch – and it's too dark to see anyway.' Meg's voice reached him through the darkness. 'No one can sleep properly, it's too cold, but come down with the rest of us here.'

He groped his way to her through the dark.

'Here.' A hand stretched up and took him by the arm. 'Watch your feet – we're all bunched up. Had any sleep at all?'

'A bit.' He did not mention the dream; he was trying to forget it.

'Get down in here.' She moved, and he fumbled his way down amid sleepy grunts from Lacey and a half-strangled snore from Bain. Their legs and bodies seemed all mixed up. 'Don't wake them.' She pulled him down. 'That better?'

He was lying between Meg and what seemed to be Lacey's shoulder and side and Bain's legs. 'Much better, thanks.' His teeth were still chattering audibly, and she put an arm round him. 'Sleep, Jason.' Her side was warm, and even Bain's knobbly knees gave him some protection. Gradually the violence of his shivering eased. 'Sleep, then,' she murmured. Jason started to mumble something, perhaps trying to thank her, but did not finish.

They were all awake long before dawn, cold, hungry and cramped, and they sat huddled and shivering until the first greyness suffused the forest. 'Come on,' Bain stood up stiffly. 'Perhaps only one more day of this.'

Jason remembered to thank Meg for fetching him down – but she was once again the old curt Meg, dismissing his stumbling thanks with: 'Warmer for us, too, Jason.' Hurriedly they saddled and loaded the mule, and as soon as they could see to move without tripping over roots and getting entangled in the trailing thorn fronds they climbed back up to the path.

Once again they spread well out as they walked, and in the same formation – Bain well forward, then Meg, Peter and last of all, Jason with the mule. They hurried along, and gradually the misery of the cold left them. All was quiet, and Angus Bain commented: 'No fighting till after breakfast!'

'Perhaps the Shans have won!'

'Maybe.'

Then they heard, very close, a propeller-driven air-craft, and Bain looked up in surprise. 'Sounds like an old T-28!'

'Burmese!' called Peter Lacey. 'It must be!' He ran along the path towards an open space. 'I'll give it a wave!'

Bain ran after him and seized him by the arm, 'Not on your life! What do you think that pilot will do when he sees us? He'll reckon we're Shans! Don't forget the Burmese are putting down a Shan rebellion!' He stared angrily at the taller man. 'What d'you think he's out looking for? That boy'll strafe us and go home and report a convoy of ammunition destroyed, and get a medal!'

'Never!' Lacey, white with pain from his arm, cried: 'He'll see we're English!'

'I'm a Scot,' snapped Bain. 'And don't be a fool. Sorry about your arm,' he added gruffly.

'He's right, Peter,' Meg's voice was edged. 'Even if he doesn't shoot us up, what can he do?' The engine roar came closer, and Jason led Jenny at a run down into the trees. The others shrank back, and the aircraft whizzed close over them heading for the east ridge.

'Let's hope the KMT are clear of that village,' said Bain grimly.

'He'll spot their weapon pits, bound to!'

'And those poor villagers –' Meg was interrupted by the thunder of two explosions, very close together. 'He's bombing that village,' she cried. 'It's full of people!'

'I told you he was looking for a target,' Bain snapped at Lacey. 'He'll attack anything that looks like troops. Now will you understand?' They stood pressed back in the shelter of the trees while the aircraft circled. Hardly had he spoken when over the ridge sounded two long hisses followed by two more explosions. 'Rockets; now for the cannons.'

'You seem to know a lot about this,' Lacey stared at Bain in no very friendly fashion.

'I've seen it all before – in Laos, Cambodia, South Vietnam –' He stopped at the noisy, jerking bump, bump, bump of cannon-fire. 'He'll go home as soon as his guns are empty,' he went on, 'but we'd better let him get clear before we move on; he may have kept a belt or two for stray targets.'

Jason listened to the bombing and Bain's bitter words with a feeling of hopelessness. Those villagers had never done anyone any harm; they grew the opium, but they didn't refine it into dope and push it in the ghettoes of New York and Detroit. Nor, for that matter, did the Akhas – yet both villages had been destroyed, and the people would be lucky if they had escaped death or wounds as well.

The T-28 circled wide above the east ridge; they heard the engine noise swell, then it faded away in the direction of the northern hills.

'Looking for convoys around Kengtung,' said Bain in gloomy satisfaction. 'I think we can get on.'

They set out again in silence. That aircraft, Jason realized, had been a blessing in disguise, for it meant that KMT patrols from that particular group would be unlikely now to go in search of possibly mythical mule-loads of heroin, not when they had just been bombed and strafed. All the same, he wished it hadn't happened; he'd rather have risked the KMT than have this sick feeling of hearing a village murdered.

So they plodded on, hour after hour, silent with their own thoughts, till Bain stopped them once again. 'See that ridge just ahead?'

To Jason it looked familiar, but then, most of the scrubby, half-overgrown hillsides with their patchy woods looked much the same. But was it –

'That's it,' he confirmed, 'the ridge just above the Akha village.' They walked on, and when near it Bain climbed to the crest, looked over, then beckoned them up to him. 'Look at this.'

He crouched at the edge of the path, peering through a screen of tall grass. The Akha village had disappeared. In its place was a series of greyish terraces, stuck about with tall, burnt poles, and heaped with smouldering ash and blackened pots. From it rose the sharp, acrid whiff of burnt thatch.

'Nothing much for us there, I'm afraid.' Bain rose and was about to walk over the ridge down towards the ashes of the village, when Jason gripped his arm. He knew suddenly that they must not go near that open, dusty, still smoking space. 'Don't go down – there may be someone there.'

Bain looked at him curiously. 'I can't see a soul!'

'They might be hiding at the edge of the village, waiting for us!'

'Who might, Jason?'

'The Haus.'

'I thought we'd worked out that they would have

cleared off by now?' Bain spoke patiently but Jason felt it was only with an effort.

'Let's just get on.' This time it was Peter who spoke, and with no pretence at patience. 'We haven't time to hang about.' His skin was yellowish again, and he licked his lips. 'Let's get on.' He was sweating, in spite of the fresh hill breeze. 'Those Haus have gone home long ago.'

'No they haven't,' said Jason. He tried to convince himself that he was not being influenced by his dream. 'They *have* got a Jap in charge, a Red Army man called Yasuno. I've come across him before. He won't give up, ever, not till he's dead or we are.' He stopped. For better or worse his secret was out.

Bain stared at him. 'If what you say is true, Jason, we must be very, very careful. You can tell me about this chap later on, but first we've got to get past this place without being seen.'

'How can we?' snapped Peter Lacey. 'It's impossible to get past unseen!'

'Oh it's possible, all right, but we'll have to do it the hard way.'

# 9
# DRAGON'S TEETH

'THERE's only one way to get round.' Bain spoke with
finality. 'That's through the forest down below here,
on this near side of the ridge.'

'It'll take hours,' Meg looked down to where the

trees grew out thickly from the slope. 'We didn't have much luck with our last attempt to get through forest – especially with the mule!'

'The boy's just guessing,' Lacey's voice was again irritable. 'This is Shan territory; the Haus wouldn't dare come back.' He took a deep breath and licked his lips. 'I think we can quite safely walk on.'

'No, Peter.' Bain was shaking his head. 'No. If Jason is right – and it *is* this man Yasuno – he is worth any effort to avoid. And suppose we *did* run into that bunch again – what on earth do you think they'd do to us? But for us they'd be safe across the Mekong by now, looking forward to sharing the best part of a million bucks. As it is, they're still here and left with nothing except maybe king-sized headaches from that datura. No,' he spoke very grimly. 'We just daren't risk it.'

'I don't feel too good,' said Lacey. He mopped his face with his left hand and again Jason noticed how he held his right arm awkwardly, as if it pained him. '*I'm* willing to risk it. You lot go round if you want to.'

'Don't be a fool, Pete!' Meg's voice was sharp and commanding.

'In any case,' said Bain, his eyes never leaving Lacey's face, 'if there's someone there and they catch you, won't they then come looking for us? No, you'll just have to come along. We *must* stick together.'

Crouched in the long grass, Jason listened to these exchanges in bewilderment. He had expected that his fears about Yasuno might be discounted, especially as a detour would add – possibly quite unnecessarily – an exhausting hour of struggle across a steep forest slope. It might also make all the difference to their reaching the gorge that same day. But for anyone even to contemplate recapture seemed to him total lunacy – and Lacey, the elegant, clever archaeologist – was showing a totally unexpected side to his nature, an ugly, selfish, rather stupid side. It could only be his illness – yes, that was it; he wasn't well and was feeling the strain, and his arm was obviously very painful.

'We're wasting time.' Bain, too, sounded as if the strain was beginning to tell on him; the precise, conversational voice had been replaced by a brusque, almost savage tone. 'I'll lead off; Meg, you come next, then Peter and Jason last with the mule. You still all right, Jason?' This last was said more naturally, with none of the abruptness he had used to Peter Lacey, and Jason nodded in relief. At least *he* wasn't being blamed for being cautious! 'All right, thanks.'

'Come on.'

Bain led them back till the ridge hid them from the ash-heaped terrace and they plunged down the grassy slope at an angle. It was slippery work and Jason tried his best to kick little footholds for the mule as he scrambled and slithered along. He was relieved when they reached the first straggling clumps of trees; though providing new obstacles at least the forest offered handholds and some sort of check against a plunge down the enormous hillside below.

As Meg had warned, their detour took them over an hour, and the four were nearly exhausted when they finally struggled up to the path little more than a mile beyond the charred timbers of the village gateway.

They sprawled to rest, the ashes of the village well out of sight. Jason looked at the loaded mule, standing with drooping head. At least it was steady walking from now on – along a path and downhill all the way. He was hungry again, and beginning to feel thirsty as well, but – he realized with a shock almost of disbelief – they were safely past that village. It had probably been empty all the time.

'Can't sit here all day.' Bain rose abruptly. 'We'll move in the same formation – and keep well apart.' He slung his Sten gun and set off briskly along the path.

'Time to go, Peter.' Meg sat up. 'It won't be long now.' She spoke reassuringly, but Lacey did not reply. 'Pete!' said Meg, more sharply, a note of concern creeping into her voice. 'Can you make it?' He looked yellowish and sweaty again, and as Jason watched in alarm gave a deep yawn. She turned to Jason: 'You lead the mule on, we'll catch up in a minute.'

'All right.' Obediently Jason began to lead Jenny past the two Laceys, but Bain came running back. 'What's the hold-up?' He looked from Meg to Peter and back to Meg again. 'Is he bad again?'

''Fraid so. You go on; he'll be all right in a minute or two.'

'Nothing doing.'

Jason looked at him in surprise; why was he suddenly being so rough with Meg?

'Nothing doing,' he repeated. 'We've no time to waste messing about. Dose him now and we'll get on.'

'Dose him?' Meg raised an eyebrow.

'Yes, dose him. You got some more, didn't you? Give it him now.'

'No.' Meg's voice shook a moment, then she stared

Bain in the face. 'No,' she said, once more self-possessed.
'This is a personal business. *You* don't have your treat-
ment for a serious illness with a crowd of gawking on-
lookers around you!' She was being deliberately and
coldly offensive, and Jason, overcome with embarrassment, muttered something and began hastily leading
the mule along the path.

'Look at him,' said Meg again, this time with a note
of real rage in her voice. 'Can't you see he's not well?'
She gestured violently at Lacey, who stood swaying by
the side of the path. He yawned widely once again,
then his head started to go back and he staggered.

'Watch out!' Bain leapt towards him. 'Watch that
gun – '

Lacey mumbled and rolled his eyes, the shotgun
began slipping from his shoulder, he made a clumsy grab
at it, missed the sling and caught it by the trigger guard,
the gun swung backwards, hit the path behind him and
exploded.

'You madman!' Bain sprang for him but Lacey sank
down on to the path across the butt of the gun. 'Carrying it cocked!' He grabbed Lacey and dragged him to
one side. 'Don't you know *anything*?' He seized the gun,
snapped open the breech, eased the loaded cartridge
back into the magazine chamber and applied the
safety catch.

'He's never handled a gun,' Meg's face was pale. 'He
doesn't know anything about these things. It's not his
fault – '

'Why the hell didn't he say so, then?' Bain was
raging. He beckoned to Jason. 'Here, Jason – *you* take
it.' He glared at Meg and at the half-conscious figure of

Lacey sprawled on the path. 'Thanks to him every villain in the place knows where we are!' For a moment Jason thought Bain was going to kick the gasping Lacey. 'Give him his shot and we'll get out of here!'

She started to speak, but he interrupted her. 'We'll cut out the pretence. Did you think I hadn't guessed that he was a junkie?'

Meg clamped her mouth shut and Jason watched, feeling rather sick. She took from the pocket of her shirt the small syringe and phial. It was half-full of water. She hesitated, but Bain said grimly: 'Get on with it.' Then, to Jason's total astonishment, she opened her shoulder-bag and from it drew a plastic packet stamped with the outline of the Globe and Tiger. She took out a fraction of the white powder, mixed a solution in the phial and filled the syringe.

Jason stole a glance at Lacey. He was stretched out, his body beginning to bend back like a bow, the feet straining downwards as if they would snap the shoe-laces and from his jaws gritting out small, animal-like groans and whimpers.

'Here, Peter, love; it's all right, Peter boy.' Gently Meg took his left arm and rolled up his sleeve, and Jason saw with a fresh surge of horror that the arm was dotted with small suppurating sores. He turned his head away, but Bain said in a dry voice: 'Don't look away, Jason; this is what the Golden Triangle's all about.' Reluctantly, with an appalled fascination, he turned his head to watch. With a deft and practised twist Meg pinched up the muscle of Lacey's inside elbow, watched to see a vein turn blue and sank the needle along it, then pressed home the plunger of the syringe. When it was empty she withdrew it, wiped away the blood oozing from Lacey's arm and rolled down and buttoned his sleeve at the wrist again.

'His other arm's gone bad, hasn't it, Meg?' Bain nodded to the swollen, awkwardly held right arm.

'Yes,' she replied curtly, once again in possession of herself.

'No nice clean boiled or sterile water for the injections after the Haus got us – wasn't that it, Meg?' Bain's tone was icy but she looked back at him quite calmly, as at someone being unnecessarily troublesome.

'That's quite correct.' She mopped Lacey's face, speaking to him softly. 'There, love, it's all right now, we'll look after you.' She held his head tenderly and Jason had a peculiar shocked feeling; sisters shouldn't speak like that to brothers! It was as if – but he jibbed at the thought. Perhaps, though, she thought of herself more as his mother. He looked at the recumbent Lacey with disgust. He *was* a menace – and what a fool to get himself hooked on dope.

'How long will he be?' Bain looked worriedly back in the direction of the burnt village. 'If Yasuno *is* back there you can be sure he will send someone to have a look along this way. They'll be careful in case Shans had fired that shot, but they'll also remember very well that we too have a shotgun.'

Jason looked down at the path. Clear and sharp, the mule's hoof prints stood out in the dust. Bain caught his eye. 'Exactly. When they reach this point they'll know we've got past once more.'

'He'll come after us,' said Jason. His mouth was dry.

'If he's there ... Well?' He looked in no very

friendly fashion at the man on the ground. 'Have you quite recovered from your little trouble?'

Jason's eyes widened and for a moment he forgot Yasuno. Peter Lacey sat on the path, breathing deeply, colour coming back to his cheeks and the old friendly smile to his eyes. 'Have I held you up?' He smiled apologetically. 'Sorry about that.' He sprang to his feet, lightly, brushing dust from his hands. 'Shall we get on?'

Jason stood gaping. It was – it was like Jekyll and Hyde! The transformation was complete.

Lacey looked round, then his eye rested on the gun slung over Jason's shoulder. 'Don't you bother with that, Jason, I'll carry it.'

'Don't you remember?' Bain was watching him with a kind of clinical curiosity. 'Here – look at this.' He bent and pointed. Where the gun had exploded a long swathe of the coarse grass bordering the path had been blasted away. Only burnt and scattered stems remained, and fragments of the cardboard cartridge case lay where they had been blown outwards from the muzzle. 'Can't you remember?' he asked again.

'Not a thing,' said Lacey, his eyes wide and innocent. 'Perhaps when I was having one of my attacks – '

Jason watched him narrowly. Did those wide, clear blue eyes suddenly look sly?

'We know all about your attacks,' interrupted Bain roughly. 'Let's get on. Jason, you follow me; Meg and Peter, come behind.' He turned on his heel and set off along the path. Jason let him get well ahead, then with a click of encouragement and a gentle tug on the leading rein, set off himself. A few yards on he glanced back

over the mule's withers. They still stood on the path,
Peter talking to Meg very rapidly. She stood without
answering, but Jason walked on with a peculiar feeling
between his shoulder-blades, and his hand stole down
to the cocking handle of the shotgun.

How many hours to the gorge? He tried to remember
exactly how long it had taken when they first walked
along this path with the Shans. It seemed like another
existence; then their climb had really been a fairly
gentle stroll up the ridge, their Shan captors friendly and
considerate. It had taken – Jason struggled to remember – not much more than two hours to climb from the
gorge to the abandoned hilltop village, and another
three to the Akha village. Now, however, they were
racing along, and downhill. He glanced back once
more; Meg and Peter were keeping up, Peter in particular as if nothing had ever been the matter with him
– indeed, even from this distance of some yards looking
fit and sparkling with health. So that was heroin,
thought Jason; with it you appeared a normal human –
without it, an animal in torment. No wonder addicts
would commit any crime for it. But if Peter was a
junkie, why wasn't Meg? He remembered lectures at
school where they were told how addicts corrupted
others, both to sell them dope for money for their own
supplies and – very nearly as compelling – to have
others sharing their hell with them. He stole another
glance around: Meg was certainly no junkie; striding
out in front of Peter, she looked every inch the stronger
character of the two. She was handsome, he admitted
reluctantly, but, oh my, she was formidable!

The path wound through patches of scraggy woods,

old ridge-top clearings and occasional open stony stretches where the view over the ridges east and west was breath-taking, but where they hurried even faster, feeling naked and exposed. At last they came within sight of the gapped roofs of the abandoned village.

Angus Bain stopped and let the others catch up. 'There's that last village ahead – we'll have a breather before we close up to it.' They rested by the path, Jason holding Jenny's rein while his mind wandered over their predicament, now so nearly resolved. On the surface all was simple: they were four fugitives with the simple aim of escape. Beneath the surface, however, he sensed strange, deep currents. He had been watching Meg, trying to puzzle it all out, when something made him turn his head – and he met the eyes of Peter Lacey, but they were no longer candid and smiling. Jason blinked: the venom in that glance surprised him – he had done nothing to Lacey! But perhaps he was mistaken, for the blue eyes, now expressionless, focused on something a little beyond Jason's head.

Bain stretched out his legs with a sigh. 'Now, Jason,' he leant round on one elbow. 'What made you think there'd be Haus in that burnt village?' He smiled: 'Not another dream, surely?'

Jason smiled back without replying. He was glad to be sitting down, even on a stony, dusty path with an ache of hunger inside him that half a dozen of Colonel Chula's breakfasts would hardly cure.

'But Yasuno now,' the correspondent went on. 'You've run across him before?'

'Yes, down in South Thailand.' With the prospect of safety only a couple of hours away Jason felt talkative

and confident. 'He was in charge of a gang of Rengo
Sekigun who hijacked a VC10 in January.'

'And you were on it?' Angus Bain was looking at him
with sharp eyes.

'Yes. I was going back to school, from Hong Kong,
after the Christmas holidays.'

'Go on.' Bain, leaning back, was watching Jason
narrowly. Meg, her face impassive, had turned her
head towards him to listen, and Lacey, eyebrows raised,
was studying Jason as if seeing him for the first time.
'Go on,' the journalist repeated.

Suddenly cautious Jason said: 'There's not a lot to
tell. I got out, and later met up with the Thais – '

'Colonel Chula.'

Jason looked up in surprise at Bain's interjection.
'How did you know that?'

'I flew down from Bangkok to cover the story.
Colonel Chula kept us journalists in our place, all
right.' He looked at Jason with open curiosity. 'We
heard from the locals that a European boy had escaped from that plane. That must have been you.'

Jason nodded. 'I got out through the hydraulic bay.'

'And did you tell the Thais about the radio link
between the hijackers and Black September?'

Jason nodded again. 'Yes. I saw their aerial direction.'

'So the failure of Yasuno's attempt to raise enough
money for his little schemes was due to you?'

'Oh, no,' said Jason vehemently. 'The Thais did it
all – and a couple of Japanese detectives. They were
splendid.'

'But you told them?'

'Yes. I told them.'

'Does Yasuno know about this?'

'No, thank God.' Jason spoke with feeling. 'Not a thing. He knows that an English boy got out – but no more.'

'Except that he was very thoroughly tricked, that all his gang but himself were killed or captured, and that he himself only got away by the skin of his teeth, with all his fine plans in ruins. Is that right?'

'Yes,' agreed Jason. 'That's about it.'

'I should think he has often wondered who was responsible, don't you?'

'Yep.' Jason was beginning to wish that he had kept his mouth shut.

'Just as well, then,' said Bain, 'that Yasuno doesn't know you are not far away.' He saw Jason's discomfiture. 'I don't think you've anything to fear from him now, we're too near Thailand. But we might as well get on, at that.' He rose. 'We'll go.'

They walked on more carefree, hurrying cheerfully down the rocky path, more rocky and open now that it neared the main shoulder of the great ridge. 'One more village to go,' sang Bain. Even Peter and Meg seemed more animated and Jason began to think that he had misjudged the archaeologist. After all, addicts *did* get cured – and Meg was certainly doing what she could to look after him! It was curious, though, that he should have dreamed about Yasuno; that was probably worry. Perhaps he *had* been in that village! If so, he was well behind. And yet . . . Jason felt that something did not quite fit, and he worried at it like a dog with an awkward bone. He tried to shrug it off; what did odd details in a dream matter? Yet it *was* curious that he should dream of Yasuno chasing him . . . He clenched his fist. That was it! He had dreamt, not of Yasuno lying in wait, but of Yasuno *following*. He looked back over his shoulder, over the mule's withers and saddle, up at the rocky patches of slope above and behind. It was ridiculous, of course, to base his actions on dreams – yet a little prudence would do no harm, surely! He slowed down again, looking back, and behind him Meg stopped and waited patiently. 'Sorry,' he said. 'I was just looking – '

'For Yasuno?'

Jason turned away again. She must think him nervous and over-imaginative. He felt a slight flush at ears and neck. He plodded on to where Bain stood crouched forward and examining the hilltop village, now little more than three hundred yards ahead and plainly in view.

'Have a good look, Jason, will you?' Angus Bain was peering rather doubtfully at the village, shading his eyes against the bright sun.

The path dipped and ran most of the way towards the village through trees, but rose again to the broken-down houses in plain and open view on their shelf-like terraces. There was certainly movement there; Jason saw one or two figures moving about between the houses, and one man whom he took to be an Akha appeared for a moment leading a pony.

'It's certainly occupied,' said Bain slowly. 'They might be Akhas from the burnt village, settling here again, but I can't be certain. What do you think, Jason?'

Jason stood up on his toes behind a tree, peering at

the little group of houses, and was about to admit that
he could not make up his mind when he saw something
that made his heart jump. It was a man, and he only
caught a fleeting glimpse of him vanishing between
two of the houses. The face was no more than a blur,
but it was the figure itself that Jason recognized, a huge
gross figure wearing not trousers but a calf-length
*lungyi*. He was gone in a moment, but Jason hissed back
to Bain: 'Fatso!'

'Eh?' Bain rose a little higher.

'Fatso – the big Shan!'

'You quite sure?' His voice held a note of doubt.
There was no sign of the big Shan, nor any other
indication of armed men.

'Of course I'm sure!' Jason spoke rather brusquely;
he himself was beginning to wonder whether that one
fleeting glimpse had been no more than an illusion.

'Well, what's all the excitement?' Peter Lacey arrived
and came sauntering forward. He glanced past them
towards the village. 'Looks empty enough – '

'Get down!' Bain grabbed him by the arm and
Lacey gasped and turned a greenish white. He sank to
his knees and the Scot muttered, 'Sorry, forgot about
your arm. But get down, anyway; we think there may
be Shans in that village.'

'What have you done to him?' Meg came running
up and Bain waved her down fiercely. 'Careful!'

'You be careful,' she retorted. 'Remember he's sick!
Have *some* decency!' She knelt by Lacey and tried to
undo the cuff of his sleeve, but he pushed her away with
his left arm. 'Let me have a look at it, Pete,' she
pleaded.

He shook his head, eyes still shut, and Bain, watching them both, said to Meg: 'We'll have to go round. Jason thinks he saw the big Shan in that village.'

'Maung Kyaw!' Her face lit up. 'He'll help us!'

'He'll help us back into a prison, you mean. Come on, Meg; there's only one place for Peter, and that's a hospital. You know that as well as I do, he can't go on like this. Look at him.' Bain jerked his head towards Peter Lacey, sitting taking deep breaths while the blood slowly returned to his face. 'He knows it too, if only he'd admit it. Come on, we'd best get going. We'll go down the path into that dip, it's pretty well wooded and the Shans won't see us. Then we can turn off and work round below them, and meet the hill path on the far side. It'll be quite a climb, but we should manage it all right.' He turned to Lacey, still taking deep breaths, but with his eyes wide open staring at the ground. 'Like a hand?'

'I'll manage,' he said in a cold expressionless voice. Jason watched him rise slowly to his feet, and was staggered to see Lacey turn and glare at him, a look full of hatred. Jason stared back in astonishment. Lacey turned away, leaving Jason with the uneasy feeling that somehow, he could not say how, he had made an enemy, and he asked himself: why me? *He* hadn't identified Lacey as a junkie, *he* hadn't spoken roughly to him or grabbed his bad arm! Was it the spite of an addict for someone still uncorrupted? Or was he, Jason, imagining things? He lengthened the leading rein. Soon, in a few hours, they'd reach water, and Jenny could drink her fill. 'We'll take it easy,' he murmured to her, and watched her ears twitch forward, then back. Bain was already a few yards ahead. Jason began to follow him when there was a sharp cry from Meg: 'Jason! Angus!' He jerked round and Bain came running back up the path. 'What is it?' He looked suspiciously at Peter, standing with a sly look in his eye.

'Look up there!' Meg pointed.

Some eight hundred yards behind them and above, the path wound over an open patch, then turned down into trees from a short, rocky crest. Silhouetted against the clear blue sky, a man in ragged black clothing was trotting steadily along this crest. He ran down and vanished where the path entered the trees. A second man, arms slightly out to keep his balance as he ran, followed, and in quick succession, a third and then two more. Jason called forward: 'Yasuno,' he panted. 'Yasuno and the Haus!'

'What!' Bain, who had been staring angrily at Peter Lacey, jerked round. 'Where are they?'

'Coming belting down the path! They're in among the trees!' He gulped. They must believe him. 'Meg saw them! She saw them first!'

'He's right, Angus.' Meg was running towards Peter. 'We'd better get a move on!'

'All right.' Bain waved to them. 'Come on. The path dips a bit – we'll go down from there! We'll have to make a run for it.' They began to trot down the path, the sacks on the mule bumping heavily. Once down among the denser tree cover, Bain stopped. 'We'll turn off here.'

Jason's heart was beating in great thuds, and he had to clear his throat before he could speak. 'He'll see where we turned off,' he gulped in a shaking voice. Yasuno would slaughter them. 'He'll catch us up in five minutes.'

'You're right, Jason.' Bain unslung his Sten. 'You lot get past the Shans and down to the river. I'll hold them as long as I can.'

Jason found his voice. 'I'll stay.' A small cold knot in his chest made it difficult for him to speak properly. He cleared his throat. 'I'll fight with you.' He licked his dry lips. He'd known that sooner or later the show-down with Yasuno would come. He unslung the shotgun.

'No.' Bain wasted no time in praise or thanks. 'I'm not letting that heroin go for anyone. Your job – ' and he stared Jason in the eye – 'is to get it down and across the river. Tell the Thais, tell the press, too. Meg, Peter, you go with him.' Bain hurried along the path, looking right and left for some suitable spot from which to ambush the Haus. He glanced back to see Peter talking busily to Meg still standing on the path, and called: 'Get a move on, Peter; think of Meg. Get her away, go on.' Bain was turning away again when Lacey said in an easy voice: 'There's no need to fight anyone.'

Bain stared: 'What do you mean?'

'We can surrender to the Shans; give them their heroin back on the mule, just as they lost it. They'd deal with those Haus in two minutes if they were ready for them.'

'And start as prisoners all over again? You must be crazy!'

'They'd let us all go in return, I'm sure.' Lacey's

voice was reasonable, with no trace of the venom he
had revealed a few minutes earlier. He spoke per-
suasively. 'They're not murderous bandits like the
Haus – they're freedom fighters! They'd show their
gratitude!'

'No!' Bain half-shouted at him. 'No one's going to
get that heroin!' He swung round to Jason. 'Get going,
and take Meg and Peter with you. Get across the river,
d'you hear?'

'All right.' Jason began to lead Jenny along the path,
looking for an easier place to get down the slope. He
felt miserable at leaving Angus, and very frightened.
Wherever they went they bumped into armed men.
Meg had been right with her dragon's teeth. He gulped.
He remembered something. 'Angus!' he called, and
broke into a run. 'Angus!' He remembered what Medea
had told the first Jason to do.

'Well?' Still walking Bain turned impatiently.

'Don't ambush them!'

Bain gave him a look of total surprise, as if to say,
'You too!'

'Don't ambush them,' Jason repeated desperately.
'Get them to fight each other!'

Bain stopped short. 'What d'you mean?'

'Dragon's teeth,' panted Jason, pulling Jenny forward. 'Meg, I mean Medea, said – '

'I know the story!' Teeth gleamed against his black
stubble. 'We'll try it – but I'll need help.' He swung
round towards Peter Lacey, then turned back to Jason
muttering, 'Never trust a junkie.'

'I'll do it.'

Bain gripped his shoulder. 'Hide below the path.

When you see them, fire towards the village. I'll be just below it, and I'll fire back. Run for it, meet us round the hill.'

'Jenny – '

'Meg must take her.'

'Conspiring, you two?' Peter Lacey had come up silently behind them.

'Change of plan,' said Bain shortly. 'Meg, will you take the mule? Jason's staying. You two come with me.'

At her startled face Jason hurriedly explained: 'Dragon's teeth, Medea.'

Her eyebrows shot up but, unconscious of his mistake, he put the rein into her hand and began looking for a place from which to shoot.

'Come on, come on!' Bain hurried the others down into the trees but called back hastily, 'Keep alert, Jason!'

Jason acknowledged with a lift of the hand then settled himself some yards below the path where he could just see the village. He checked the safety catch of the shotgun and stood waiting for Yasuno and the Haus.

## 10

# THE CHOICE

JASON stared across at the village. It was a good hundred yards from him, but it seemed frighteningly close – and he himself was too close to the path. He moved down a yard or two to another tree, lifted the shotgun – and then remembered with a jump of the heart that it was still unloaded. Quickly he pulled back the cocking handle, felt it catch the metal rim of a cartridge and thrust it forward into the breech, then applied the safety catch with his thumb.

He still felt uncomfortably close to the path and was about to go down farther when from the corner of his eye he caught movement; someone was padding swiftly along the path above. Jason flattened himself against his tree, peered up and saw a sallow man in ragged black. It was Moustache. In a few moments he would reach the edge of the trees, then Jason himself would fire and run. It was simple enough.

But Moustache did not go out into the open. He stopped, and Jason saw his mouth open in an exclamation. Still with his eyes on the ground Moustache walked to the edge of the path, staring at it and then down the slope. Jason stood terrified. Was the Hau smelling him out? He clutched the shotgun, saw Moustache kneel and examine the ground and realized that he had seen the heavy, deep hoofprints of the loaded mule. Moustache would wait for the others and would then lead them down the tracks, which passed not ten feet behind Jason's tree. There was only one thing to do. Jason lifted the shotgun, pointed it somewhere up above the path, and pulled the trigger.

The roar of the shot and Moustache's somersault for cover seemed simultaneous and Jason caught a fleeting glimpse of a pair of heels in dirty canvas shoes vanishing over the far side of the path. Without waiting for a second look Jason swung the shotgun towards the village. For a split second it seemed empty – then the enormous figure of Fatso bounded out and stood staring across towards him, with other Shans running out behind.

Jason saw Fatso outlined huge against the shotgun barrel and his finger took the first pressure – then he aimed a fraction higher, fired twice in quick succession and saw the mountain of flesh spring sideways and crash straight through the sagging wall of the nearest house, while the other Shans scattered nimbly for cover. In a moment the village seemed empty again – then, burst on rapid burst, automatic fire from Angus Bain's Sten hammered out from just below the houses and crackled along the ridge path. Two or three figures hurrying forward along it flung themselves to the ground and Jason slipped away downhill.

Once among the bigger trees he turned and, running like a stag, sprang and raced across the slope. A shallow, dry gully seamed the hillside below where he judged the village to be; he sprang into it, ran along just under the bank – and there were Meg and Peter with the mule. 'Come on,' he gasped to them. 'They've seen the mule tracks.' His chest was heaving and he was very nearly speechless. He barely looked up as Bain came slithering down with a rush of small stones and earth. 'You all right, Jason?' Bain looked uphill, Sten gun ready. Above them a carbine crackled, firing along the path, a second opened fire and then a third.

Jason gestured, gulping and breathless: 'They were going to turn down along the mule tracks.'

'Tchha!' hissed Bain, then wrinkled his eyes. 'You certainly started something!' The last words he had to shout, and Jason blinked upwards. The scattered bursts had given way to a roar of firing. 'It's the Shans, they're trigger-happy – but that should hold the Haus for a bit. Come on.' He led off down the gully. 'We'll get round to the path as quick as we can!'

Sporadic firing continued as they made their way below the hilltop village – bursts of Sten-gun fire from the Haus, once the whup-up of Yasuno's heavy pistol, but mostly the tearing rattle of the Shan carbines. Gradually it slackened and by the time the fugitives reached the path some hundreds of feet below the village, all was quiet. They paused a minute and Jason, panting with exertion, asked: 'Can we give the mule a spell? She's very thirsty.' His own mouth was dry as dust, but he looked at Jenny with pity and some alarm. 'She may not go much farther.'

'Last lap, Jason.' Bain, resting on his haunches, looked up. 'Two hours and we're there, *and* with the heroin.' He straightened up. 'Come on. The Shans have seen off the Haus.'

Jason followed him down the steep twisty path with no sense of triumph, only of relief. It had been a messy, exhausting business and it had revealed unpleasant things, rather – he grimaced – rather like turning over a stone and finding what lay beneath.

Going down was almost worse than going up, and with their sore feet and broken shoes they slithered and stumbled and occasionally fell. Their pace was very slow, and Jason looked anxiously at the mule; the heavy loads swung and bumped and more than once at particularly steep sections he feared he would see her slip and go rolling down, with the loads carrying her down even faster. Meg and Peter seemed to be falling rather behind, and once or twice Bain called to them sharply to get a move on. 'I'm not too easy about that fellow Peter,' he confided to Jason in a low voice. 'We'll have to keep an eye on him when we get across.'

'He won't do anything!' Jason was more concerned with his feet, his thirst – he'd have given anything for an ice-cold lemonade with some salt in it – and his hunger; Peter Lacey seemed the least of their troubles. 'What can he do, anyway?'

'I don't know.' Bain sounded uneasy. 'You never know with these junkies – they'd sell their grand-mothers.'

'What's *his* worry? Once he's back he can get cured!'

'The Thai police will want to know where he's been getting his dope this last year – and they may have a few other questions to ask him as well.'

They stopped talking as they reached another steep section of the winding path, and Bain and Jason were going down it with painful care when they heard a call from behind, a low call in a strained voice: 'Angus – wait a minute!' Meg hurried to catch them up and they waited with weary impatience, glad to pause yet fearful of wasting time.

'What is it, Meg?' Bain spoke with resignation, and Jason knew what he was thinking: Lacey was in dif-ficulties again. 'Is it Peter?'

'Yes.' Her lip trembled and she looked away from them.

'All right. I'll give him a hand.' Bain was turning to climb back up the path when she said: 'You don't understand. Peter's gone!'

'Gone?'

'He ran away uphill.' She swallowed and said in a shaking voice: 'He's gone back to the Shans!'

'What!' Bain gaped at her and Jason frowned. She must be mistaken. 'The Shans?' repeated Bain. 'What for?' Then his tone changed and he said savagely: 'When did he go, Meg? How long's he been gone?'

'About three minutes.'

'And you didn't tell us – you just let us walk on!'

'I thought – ' She looked helplessly at him.

'You thought I'd shoot him? Well you were right. But it's too late now.' He swung round. 'Jason – we'll give them a fight for it! He can't reach them for another thirty minutes, but once he does they'll come down after us very fast.'

'Can't we run for it?' asked Jason. He began to feel rather sick.

Bain shook his head. 'They'll get us from above before we reach the ford.'

'You don't understand,' called Meg again, despairingly. 'They don't want to harm us!' She pointed to the two sacks. 'All they want is that!'

Bain stared at her. 'Do you believe that?' he demanded. 'Do you honestly believe that they'd simply take the heroin and then wave us goodbye?' He turned away a moment, and Jason thought he was going to choke. Bain swung round again. 'The Shans want that heroin, but they want hostages too. You and Peter would do nicely. Jason and I have been an embarrassment from the very beginning. But if we were shot we'd have been of some use by helping to put pressure on the Thais! We wouldn't tell any tales, either!' He stared at her. 'I'm beginning to see it now; that's why you gave him a good start! And you were to persuade us to surrender without a fight!'

'No!' she cried, putting out a hand to him. 'It's not like that!'

He flung her hand away. 'Isn't it?'

'I couldn't stop him!'

'Maybe so,' Bain sneered. 'But you're going to be all right whatever happens. Your precious brother will see that *you* don't get hurt.' He took a long breath, then said in a quieter voice: 'You two were in the racket with the Shans, weren't you?'

Jason had been watching and listening helplessly, and at this terrible question he stared at Meg; surely she'd deny it, say it was rubbish, nonsense, impossible – but he saw with a shock of disbelief that she was looking down at the ground. 'Yes,' she admitted in a low, flat voice. 'But I don't want any more to do with it.'

'You haven't much choice, Meg, you're in it up to the neck. Now you'd better get up the hill yourself. Tell them that we're going on down but that we're going to fight if they follow. Go on.'

'I do have a choice.' She was calm once more. 'I'm going with you.'

Bain looked at her narrowly. 'You may get hurt, Meg.'

'I've been hurt already.'

'I see. Well, that's enough talk. Let's go.'

They set off again, scrambling down the hill path with desperate urgency, but in a few minutes Bain stopped. 'They'll catch us, and we won't be ready.'

Meg drew him aside and said in a low voice: 'You're

condemning the boy, Angus. Send him on while we wait. There's no sense in him staying.'

'I don't think he'll go, but I'll ask him.' Bain then called to Jason. 'Will you go ahead and tell the Border Police where we are, Jason? They're bound to be down at the ford!'

'But what about you and Meg?'

'Oh, we won't be too far behind. I'll look after the mule. You get down there, fast.'

'No.' Jason spoke stubbornly. 'Let Meg go. She can tell them.'

'I told you, Meg,' said Bain.

'Now *you* have a choice, Angus!' She pointed to the sacks of heroin. 'Without that load we might just make it to the ford. At least we could get away into the forest. And there's another thing – the Shans will have Peter. He's enough. They wouldn't follow us simply to murder us, you *know* that. Yasuno might, but he's gone! You know what to do, Angus.'

'Leave it for them?' Bain shook his head violently. 'No. No, I won't let them have it.'

'In that case they'll get us *and* the heroin.' She sounded indifferent. She began to walk downhill, and Bain followed her, arguing: 'Eighty kilos of junk – how many lives will *that* take? *Eighty kilos!*'

Again she shrugged. 'It's your choice.'

'We *must* try.' Bain quickened his pace. 'Come on, Jason – get a move on!'

'Jenny can't do it, she *can't* go any faster!' Jason, leading rein taut, threw him an anguished glance. 'She's worn out.'

Bain stopped, took a deep breath and in a despairing voice said: 'All right, then. We'll leave it.' He stood for a moment looking at the loaded mule. 'Tether her at the edge of the path.'

'No.' Jason spoke stubbornly. 'We may have to leave them the stuff, but I'm not going to leave them Jenny. They'll drive her back uphill, they probably won't water her, or – '

'All right,' broke in Bain. 'Just unload.' They swung off the sacks.

'They'll have to carry them up themselves!' Jason gave a feeble smile.

'That's something.' Taking each sack in turn they lifted them on to the middle of the path. 'Heavy,' grunted Bain.

Jason straightened up. Yes, it was a heavy load – eighty kilos of death and misery, plus a million dollars for a few racketeers and a handful of Burmese rupees for the villagers.

'Coming, Jason?' Bain looked, not defeated, but suddenly very tired, and in that moment Jason, seeing the deep lines in the cheeks above the four-day growth of beard, realized just how much they had all depended on him, how hard he had tried and how nearly succeeded. As well as the heroin he was losing the journalistic scoop of a lifetime. Jason looked at Meg: *she* had taken a packet of the heroin from a tin – why shouldn't Bain take one as well?

'Angus!' he called. 'Take a packet of it! That'll be something for the Thai police!'

'Yes!' He ran to the sacks, but Meg said, 'You'll need this.' From the flap hip pocket of her jeans she drew a short steel nail file.

Bain looked from it to her. 'Was that how you opened the lid yesterday?'

'That's how.'

He took it and began unknotting the ropes. 'Get back up the path a bit, Jason,' he ordered. 'Keep a look out.'

'I'll do that,' offered Meg, and at Bain's glance, full of hostility and suspicion, she shrugged: 'I could have gone too, but I didn't. I had an idea he might go off, and I'd been trying to talk him out of it.'

Jason looked up from the ropes. 'Was that what you'd been arguing about earlier, back along the path?'

'That was it.'

Bain hesitated, then said curtly: 'All right, Meg. Give us as much warning as you can.' He turned back to the knots, but Jason watched the stocky, solitary figure in dirty jeans and opium-stained shirt climb up to the path. Suddenly she looked bereft, and he fell to slackening the tight knots with an uncomfortable feeling that he had just observed a shattering personal tragedy.

'Here's how Meg did it.' Bain broke into his thoughts. 'She simply dragged these two ropes apart and prised the lid off one of the tins. Just heave.'

They pulled on the ropes, unfolded the sack mouth from the two tins and Bain levered up one of the lids. 'There you are, Jason, have a last look.' He lifted out one of the white packets and slipped it into the pocket of his bush shirt. 'They won't know that one's gone.' An identical packet lay beneath it. 'I wonder if the others have all the same trademark?' He lifted out another.

'Have we time?' Jason was nervous. What if the

Shans came bounding down while they were opening the tins? 'We might get caught again.' The thought of being recaptured within sight of freedom was almost unbearable. 'Have we time?' he repeated anxiously.

'Lacey's been gone about ten minutes. It'll take him another twenty to climb up to the Shans, so we've got a little time.' Bain took out another packet, revealing an identical one below. 'They're the same all the way down.' He began fitting the lid back on, but Jason took his sleeve. An idea was forming in his mind, a trick, a common, childish trick. 'Angus – let's try a switch.' He spoke hastily, it seemed a ridiculous idea, but – 'Empty out the heroin,' he hissed. 'Fill the tins with earth, put one packet on top –' Bain was looking at him, eyes narrowed, as if Jason had suddenly taken leave of his senses, but when he spoke it was to say: 'Earth's too heavy.'

'A mix, then; some earth, some leaf mould –

'Right – but away from the path.' They opened the sacks wide, took out the tins and carried them one by one into the trees, dumping them on the lip of a narrow gully on the slope. Bain then levered off the lids while Jason tipped the packets out into a great heap on the ground.

'We'll fill the tins first,' ordered Bain, and they began scraping up the dry earth and leaf mould with their hands and pouring it into the tins. It was slow work, and in a minute or two Jason said anxiously: 'It's going to take too long.'

'Keep going,' said Bain, but they both turned at a faint gasp. Meg stood behind them, staring down at the great heap of heroin packets.

'What is it?' Bain sprang up. 'Anyone coming?'

She shook her head, still staring down at the heroin. 'No – I just couldn't make out what was happening.'

'We're going to do a switch,' explained Jason, still desperately stuffing earth into the tins. 'We'll put a packet on top to fool them.' He paused a minute, looked at his hands then resumed his frantic scraping.

'You won't manage it like that,' said Meg, 'but I think I see something . . .' She ran along the edge of the gully and pointed down. 'Here!' She waved to them. 'Rotten wood – enough for all those tins, and the weight's about right.' She was standing by a great fallen branch, soft and spongy and covered with fungi. She broke off a large chunk and held it up. 'What about this?'

'Perfect!' Bain ran up and began breaking off armfuls of the rotting wood. 'Come on, Jason, we'll make it yet.' He was stuffing it into his tin when he called out: 'No wonder it's rotten. White ants, the inside's crawling with them.' He reached across for another tin. 'Nearly finished – keep watch again, Meg, will you?'

'Right, Angus.'

'How are your tins, Jason?'

'Ready – just room for a couple of packets.'

'A couple?'

'Safer with two, in case they lift one out.'

Carefully they put two packets inside the top of each tin, Bain first making a tiny puncture on the under side of each with the nail file, muttering, 'The damp'll soon get in.' He then replaced the lids carefully and they brushed the tins free of earth and fragments. 'All clean? Right – back into the sacks with them.' They were drenched with sweat and hoarse with thirst, and the sun beat down on the open path, but they worked with frantic haste, roping up the sacks and stacking them prominently several yards back uphill.

'Now the heroin.' They raced back to the gully, and as Bain punctured each bag with the nail file Jason tossed it down, and they finished by scraping earth roughly over the pile to hide it. 'There,' gasped Bain. 'Let's get out of here.' He raced up the path for Meg and the two came hurrying down, with Bain calling, 'Quick Jason – Meg's seen something!'

Pulling Jenny he began to run downhill till Meg gasped, 'Not down the path – they'll see us from above!'

'You're right!' Bain stopped short, and after a hasty glance back uphill gestured violently to the side. They turned off, plunged into the shelter of the trees and were making their way hastily along the lip of the same little gully where they had thrown the heroin when Bain, who was coming last, hissed to them: 'Hide, quick! Get down!'

Jason sprang down into the gully, dragging Jenny with him, and Meg jumped down beside him. Bain, on hands and knees behind a tree, crouched looking back at the path, stretches of it clearly visible in the glare of the sunlight and the sacks only eighty yards from them. 'Leading man coming down fast,' he reported without turning his head. 'He'll see the sacks in a minute.'

Meg and Jason lay flattened out, eyes just above the earth edge. In a moment they too saw the first man just as he caught sight of the sacks – but lost sight of him as he sprang to the side.

For some moments there was silence, then they heard

a voice calling, a warning voice, and a brief reply from farther uphill. The first man appeared again, moving down very cautiously along the path, head turned away from them as he stared suspiciously at the two roped bundles. There was more movement higher up, and two figures came walking down, also very cautiously, and Jason felt Meg clutch his arm with a sharp intake of breath, for one, although at first only visible in outline, was tall and moved with a slender elegance beside the stocky figure next him.

The three figures came out into the sunlight and stood looking down at the sacks, and this time it was Jason's turn to feel his breath choke in his throat and his stomach contract. The tall man was Peter all right, but the two men with him wore ragged black clothing. The first, a sallow man carrying an ancient Sten gun, had a small black moustache, and the second, who had an automatic pistol in his hand, was Yasuno.

'Peter – ' gulped Meg.

From his tree above the gully Bain heard her. 'He didn't make it to the Shans, Meg,' he said gently, in the faintest of whispers. 'The Haus got him first.'

## II

## THE SACRIFICE

THE three lay staring from the shadows at the men in
the sunlight. Yasuno, hefting his pistol in his hand, stood
staring down at the two roped sacks then at the mule's
hoofprints, leading away down the path. Moustache,
head craning this way and that, gazed about him sus-

piciously, and Peter stood stock-still, his right arm across his chest and supported by his left. At this distance – well over eighty yards – Jason could not make out his expression, but his strained, rigid posture revealed his fear. Peter's plight was desperate – but it was to Yasuno that their eyes kept returning.

'He smells a rat!' Bain's whisper floated to them. 'Don't move!'

Yasuno did indeed smell a rat. For some moments he stood looking from the sacks to the path to Peter and back to the sacks again. He took a few paces along the path, eyes on the ground, then turned back again, as if reluctant to go too far away from them – and at last he signalled and the other three Haus came very cautiously down. One of them, more wary than the others, bent peering down into the trees as if he might come down to where the three lay hidden – till Yasuno gave a curt order and this man ran back uphill again. 'The look-out,' breathed Bain.

At a gesture from Yasuno Peter knelt and began pulling at the ropes around one sack while the others stood back.

'Yasuno's taking no chances,' whispered Bain. 'He suspects a booby-trap.'

The same fear had come to Jason and he lay quivering with a desperate anxiety to get away before they emptied the tins. Now, when the Haus all had their eyes fixed on those sacks, now was surely the moment to steal away down the gully – but one mistake, one cracked branch, and they would join Peter. He was making little headway, unable with his one good arm to heave the ropes far enough apart, and at last, with a gesture of angry impatience the Japanese drew his dah, pushed Peter aside and with two swift slashing cuts severed the ropes. Peter then hurriedly opened the sack mouth and Yasuno put the point of his dah under one lid, levered it up and jumped back.

Nothing happened. He stepped forward again, peered in and with his left hand lifted the corner of the top packet. He paused, then jerked the packet out. Feeling rather sick Jason waited for him to lift the second packet and discover what lay beneath – but Yasuno instead turned his attention to the second tin, again levering up the lid with his dah point, to see the familiar packet on top. Moustache, pointing uphill, began speaking urgently to him. Yasuno drew away impatiently – then nodded, beckoned, and the Haus pulled out the tins, hastily bundled up sacks and cut ropes and threw them in among the trees.

The three Haus lifted a tin each, and Yasuno turned to Peter and pointed to the fourth. Peter shook his head violently, pointing to his right arm, and then up the hill, and Jason saw from his gestures that he was arguing that they should leave him with the Shans. Yasuno put the dah to Peter's chest and with his left hand again pointed to the tin and in a sharp command that reached Jason's ears barked: 'You take!'

Peter Lacey dropped his arms, looked down the path towards the gorge, took a deep breath – Jason saw his shoulders rise and fall – and began to speak very slowly and with careful gestures. As Yasuno watched and listened he gradually lowered the point of the dah, but his eyes never left the tall man's face. Moustache, looking repeatedly uphill, interrupted once or twice, but Yasuno ignored him. Jason felt his blood run cold. Peter was betraying him as the boy of the hijack, offering Yasuno revenge in exchange for his own freedom – and Jason saw too the evil simplicity of it, for if Yasuno followed he would spare none of the three. With Meg, Bain and Jason all dead Peter Lacey could return, the sole – and innocent – survivor.

Again Moustache spoke, but still the Japanese ignored him, turning away to stare down the path towards the gorge, while Lacey watched with folded arms. Yasuno took a pace or two, and Jason saw his face in the sharp sunlight – pale as marble, and as hard.

Then Moustache seized Yasuno's arm and, as if in a dream, he turned and looked at the heroin on the path – and, as if awakening suddenly, sheathed the dah and again gestured to Lacey. Slowly, awkwardly, almost despairingly, Peter lifted the heavy tin – then flung it at Yasuno, catching him in the chest and sending him staggering, thrust Moustache aside and ran, dodging the other Haus and swerving away from the clutch of the look-out. Yasuno sprang to his feet, lifted his pistol, waited till Lacey was clear of the others and fired two shots. The hollow whup-up of the forty-five echoed out and Peter Lacey's head snapped back as the bullets punched between his shoulder-blades. His legs took one or two short steps, but his knees buckled under him and he struck the ground with a thump and lay absolutely still. Without a second glance Yasuno called the look-out and he snatched up the fallen tin.

'They've murdered him!' Meg leaned over and, before Jason could stop her, snatched up the shotgun and levelled it at Yasuno's back.

Jason watched her, petrified. If he grabbed her the gun would go off – and at this range the buckshot would no more than sting him. Jason sat speechless, not daring to move. Meg's finger tightened on the trigger – then slowly uncurled. She slid back down, let the gun fall sideways and Jason caught it by the barrel as it fell. Her eyes were open but tears poured down her cheeks, and she lay sobbing silently, her head turning from side to side, and making no attempt to cover her face.

Still clutching the shotgun Jason looked back up over the edge of the gully. The four Haus, each loaded with a tin, were hurrying back towards the shoulder of the hill, and finally Yasuno, with a last look round, ran after them.

'Don't move,' whispered Bain. 'Let them get clear.'

For long moments they lay staring through the screening leaves at the motionless body of Peter Lacey and the loaded and hurrying figures of the Haus, as one by one they reached the short skyline and ducked away from the path into the trees. Last was Yasuno, who paused to look back downhill, at this distance his face a pale blur, just as Jason had first seen it pressed against the glass of the aircraft flight deck. Then the stocky figure swung around and vanished into the trees, but Jason remained crouching, as if hypnotized, gazing up at where Yasuno had gone.

'Come on.' Bain prodded him. 'The Shans'll be bound to send someone down to check on those shots.' He rose to his feet. 'Come on, Meg, we must go. Here.' He bent and took her arm, talking quietly all the time. 'Come on, lass, we've got to get moving. We daren't wait, or the Shans'll get us.' He pulled her to her feet, and she stood in the gully, head down and unmoving, as Bain went on: 'We couldn't do anything about Peter, you know that. You do know that, Meg, don't you?' he repeated, speaking very gently.

'Yes, I know.' She wiped her face with her sleeve and looked up at him. 'I know.' She began to climb out of the gully, but up its forward slope, back up towards the path. 'Help me with him.'

'Where are you going?' Bain threw an anguished glance past her towards the sprawled body and the empty skyline beyond. 'We've got to get down to the gorge!'

'We must take Peter.' Meg spoke with a kind of loving grief. 'We can bury him at Nakhon Wat, where he was so happy.' She walked blindly out on to the path. 'We can take him on the mule.'

'No!' Bain ran after her and seized her arm. 'No, we can't! The mule's beat, we haven't a minute to waste, those Shans'll soon be down on us – ' As she struggled to get away he wrenched her round and shook her: 'Will you listen, Meg? Do you want to kill us all?' At that she stopped, and Angus hissed over his shoulder to Jason: 'Get going, boy – get on down, d'ye hear?'

'Okay, all right – ' Jason scrambled out of the gully and set off downhill, towing the mule by its leading rein and mechanically avoiding the loose stones on the path. The death of Peter had shocked him, but he felt depressed almost beyond reason by this last little piece of harshness. Did Angus *have* to shake Meg like that when she had just seen her brother murdered? He glanced back. A little way behind the mule came Meg, her smudged face blank with despair; behind her again came Angus, Sten gun at the ready, and a good hundred yards back up the path Jason caught his last glimpse of Peter, a foreshortened hump in the dust of the sunlit path. The crest and skyline were still empty, with no sign of pursuing Shans. 'Come on, Jenny.' He twitched at the rein and continued his weary plod downhill.

The sight of the river getting closer and the first sounds of the rushing water made their thirst seem intolerable, and when the mule swung her head and whinnied at the first tiny stream a little way in from the path, they limped hastily towards it and flung themselves down to drink.

When Jason had drunk his fill he rolled over, sated, to watch the mule drink and drink, till at length she snorted her satisfaction and after blowing on the surface of the water once or twice, lifted her head and snuffled at his ear.

'Ahh!' Bain sighed. He lay flat on his back for a few moments, then pushed himself up on one elbow. 'How are you, Meg; feel any better?'

She nodded. She was bathing her swollen face in the cold water and when she had dried it roughly with the remnants of a handkerchief she moved away from the little stream and sat down by herself.

'We'll have a five-minute break,' said Bain with a warning glance at Jason. No one spoke for a minute, then Meg herself broke the silence. 'At least he won't be a prisoner,' she said in a muffled voice.

'That's been worrying you for a long time, hasn't it?'

She nodded. 'He'd have lost his reason in prison – he had such a fine mind.'

'I know the pattern, I'm afraid – brilliant student, exams all too easy, a bit bored, so smoking pot at parties, pot losing its kick, then on to LSD, coke, anything for a stronger kick, till finally the hardest stuff of all – heroin. That began with him in Turkey, didn't it?'

She nodded again. 'It all seems so long ago.'

'I read about it, of course – drugs trouble on a site near the Black Sea. You had to leave, didn't you?'

'Yes. It was more or less hushed up.'

'Then you got yourselves fixed up with a site here.'

She sighed. 'You seem to know a lot about it.'

'I've been chasing up this drug traffic for years – and until only a couple of years ago Turkey was one of the main sources of raw opium. You'd mentioned digs there yourself, so I began to think back a bit, and put two and two together. But *you* were never a junkie, Meg. What were you doing – looking after Peter? Trying to break him of it?'

'He was brilliant!' she burst out. 'He'd have got better, I'm certain he would!'

'Not out here, he wouldn't, Meg.' Bain spoke very gently, and without raising his voice asked, 'How did Peter get involved in all this?'

She sighed, a long weary sigh. 'He's dead now, you might as well know . . . Peter heard of this site, and thought it might be the original Nakhon Wat. No one believed him.' She shrugged. 'We had no funds ourselves and no organization would provide any. But then we got the offer of cash backing – regular payments, and money for the finest equipment. In return we were to allow certain supplies to be brought into the camp, and packed in the crates we sent to Bangkok. They knew all about Peter; he was to get supplies of heroin –'

'The purest,' nodded Bain. 'Sorry, go on.'

' – and for no payment. It was all too tempting.' Meg sighed. 'It was wrong, but if he didn't do it the drug runners would soon find someone else and at least this gave him the chance to identify Nakhon Wat – a discovery in its way like Angkor.'

Jason drew a deep breath. Now he knew why Peter had hated him. Not only was he a friend of the police chief, but by turning up at Nakhon Wat at the wrong moment he and Angus had ruined Peter's plans.

After a pause Bain asked: 'Who was behind it, Meg?'

She shook her head. 'Pete never told me – he said I'd better not know.'

'Did you have any clue?'

'It was someone in Government, someone with plenty of influence and probably power, too.' She gave a cold smile. 'He isn't poor, either. We must have had nearly a quarter of a ton of heroin pass through, mainly in small shipments, but this last one was the big one.'

'But then the fighting started, and the Shans were in trouble. The Burmese were pressing them on their side and the Thai border was soon going to be swarming with police. They couldn't get the heroin across, yet they daren't wait – hence the need for hostages, to exchange for a safe conduct through to Laos. Wasn't that it?'

'Yes.' Meg nodded. 'That's just how it was.'

'And it's always possible that the man who might have to recommend that a safe conduct be given was actually the organizer of the drug-running in the first place!' Bain wrinkled his brows. 'Now, who can it be?' Then he asked: 'Does the name Chula mean anything to you?'

Jason listened with a sinking heart. It couldn't be, yet it all fitted.

'I've met him once or twice,' replied Meg. 'Why?'

'Could he be the man?'

'I suppose he could. I don't know.'

It was clear that she did not greatly care. Bain stood up. 'We've had a breather and no one's come chasing past. Let's go.'

Bain stopped them when they were still short of the gorge. 'I'll just have a look.' He returned in a few minutes. 'There are men in khaki on the far side.'

'Border Patrol!' Jason was exuberant. 'We've made it!' He was about to hurry on down when Bain stopped him. 'How can you be so sure we've made it?'

'There are no Shans on that side!'

'I know that – but who is the man the Shans are running the stuff to?'

'We don't know.'

'Suppose he's across there now? You can get some very unfortunate accidents at border crossings. Someone might just make what's called a tragic mistake.'

'You mean Colonel Chula?' Jason was outraged. 'He wouldn't harm us!'

'I'm naming no one, Jason – but whoever it is won't have his little game spoiled by three unimportant foreigners. I think we'd better cross somewhere else. Can you swim? Oh, of course – you're the chap who swam away from the hijackers. What about you, Meg?'

'Yes.' She sounded indifferent, as if it was immaterial to her whether she survived the crossing or not.

They climbed across the slope and, when well out of sight of the ford, dropped down to the water's edge. 'Just as well it hasn't rained.' Bain had to shout above the roar of water. 'Another week and this'd be twenty feet higher, with trees coming down like matchsticks!'

Jason examined the water with a swimmer's eye. It was fast and deep, but possible. 'First we'll strip *you*,' he said to Jenny, removing her pack saddle and replacing her bridle with headstall and rein. Saddle and bridle he heaved behind a bush: 'Let the Shans find them,' he grunted to himself.

'We'd be better off without these things as well, Jason.' Bain held up his Sten and nodded at Jason's shotgun.

'Are you sure?' Jason felt very doubtful.

'They'll be a nuisance in the water, and once across and into Meg's camp we won't need guns, now, will we?'

'No, I suppose not.'

'Come on, then.' Bain flung the Sten into the deepest part of the greeny-white water, and Jason, unloading the shotgun, took it by the barrel, swung it like a hammer-thrower and let go. It soared out, seemed to hang in the air and dropped into the water with hardly a splash. 'Excalibur,' he murmured. Suddenly he felt defenceless.

'I'll go first.' Bain waded into the water and struck out, was plucked along by the current but reached the far bank safely thirty yards downstream, and waved them across. Jason knew that he could make it without undue difficulty, but Meg – how would she fare? He turned to her. 'Perhaps we'd better swim together, Meg. It might be safer – and Jenny, she'll be a help.'

Meg shrugged her shoulders. 'Come on, then.'

Leading the mule he followed Meg into the water and was relieved to see her swim strongly, and they too reached the far side safely and scrambled out, wet and dripping, on to the rocky edge.

'We're not too far from the camp,' said Bain. 'Looks as if we've made it.'

'Home again,' said Meg with a bitter smile.

They reached the first of the ruins within half an hour, and Meg called, 'Nearly there! We've the pyramid temple next, then the central temple, and it's just beyond that.' They walked on, and at the pyramid Jason recognized the great edifice with the serpent-carved lintel. He wondered vaguely what lay inside it but his mind dwelt more on food, and he hurried on behind the others till they came to the camp.

The long thatched huts were just as they had last seen them, but the cookhouse by the stream was silent, and no smoke rose. Meg lifted an eyebrow: 'Hardly surprising: there's nothing to keep Cookie here. But what about the police?'

'Someone's been here, all right.' Bain pointed to the tyre marks in the dust. 'Medium-sized trucks – Border Patrol, most likely.'

'Those'd be the men we saw by the river.'

'Probably. Anyway, we'd best walk on to Ban Phao; it's not far.'

'There's the camp telephone,' said Meg. 'We can ring the Rest House.'

'Wonderful! They can get the police to send a jeep for us.'

'And the cook can put on some lunch – or is it supper?'

At Jason's suggestion Bain threw back his head and laughed and even Meg's heavy face showed the quiverings of a smile. To cover his embarrassment Jason busied himself hitching Jenny's rein to a bamboo post while Bain forced open the bamboo-frame door. In a minute they heard the crank-crank-crank of the telephone handle and Bain's voice speaking in Thai – then suddenly changing to English. 'Mr Varalak! *You* up here?'

Faintly the voice came through from the other end, and Bain replied, 'Not Peter, I'm afraid. He's dead.'

There was a long pause, then a crackle of questions which Bain interrupted with: 'First could you ask the police to send a jeep or something? We've had nothing to eat – ' Again he listened and eventually said, 'Fine. See you in a few minutes.' He put down the phone and came out. 'Varalak,' he explained. 'Says he came up from Bangkok as soon as he heard about this business. As the UN man he felt responsible for the archaeologists. He's coming for us himself.'

Jason asked, 'What'll happen to the mule? I promised her a good feed!' He gave a rather shame-faced laugh, but Meg, quite seriously, said, 'You're right, Jason. Try the kitchen; if you look in the store cupboard you may well find something for her.'

He hurried down to find it empty but for half a

dozen small sacks. He opened the first to see coarse white flour, then the next to see faintly withered chilli pods – but the third was half full of split peas, some already sprouting. 'Jenny you're in luck!' His eye fell on a basin, much battered, with the white enamel chipped black, but just the right size. Into it he heaped split peas, a little salt and several handfuls of flour, and mixed it all up thoroughly. At last, the bowl in both hands, he made his way carefully up to the others just as a jeep pulled up sharply in front of him and Varalak, immaculate in a light suit, jumped out.

'My dear Jason.' He held out his hand, and Jason put the bowl carefully on the bonnet of the jeep, dusted his hands, and returned the handshake. 'So you returned safely!' Varalak's smile was full of sympathy and concern.

Meg and Bain came running over, and she said breathlessly, 'Oh, Mr Varalak – Peter's dead!' She was blinking back her tears and Bain said, 'I think we'd better get Miss Lacey out of this as quickly as possible, Mr Varalak. She's had a very rough time.'

'Of course, of course.' Varalak nodded, wrinkling his eyes up and shaking his head. 'I must just have a word with Miss Lacey.' He drew her aside and said in a lower voice, 'Did Peter leave any message for me before he died?'

'About what, Mr Varalak?' Bain sounded impatient. 'Really I think that – '

'Yes, yes. Of course.' Varalak interrupted, ducking his head apologetically. 'You must forgive me, I've been so worried about you – and to hear that you'd

been abducted by the Haus, that was terrible. I expect
they killed Peter?'

There was a pause, then Bain said quietly, 'Who told
you about the Haus, Mr Varalak?'

Varalak did not answer. He was staring past them,
and Jason saw that his eyes were fixed on the mule.
Bain, watching him, said, 'You know about the mule,
Mr Varalak. You also know about the Haus. How do
you know about these things? Is that why you came up
here, in case we *had* got the load across?'

Varalak stared at him, then at Meg, whose face
showed dawning realization, at Jason, and back to
Bain again.

'Angus!' called Meg sharply. 'He's got a gun!' She
gave Varalak a shove, he staggered and the small automatic pistol in his hand cracked out and the bullet
clanged off the jeep. He lifted the pistol again and
Jason, with a cry of 'Here!', jerked the basin of floury
fodder straight into his face. Varalak gave a choking,
crowing gasp. His eyes, full of flour, were screwed tight
shut, but blindly he swung the pistol, and Bain roared
'Scatter!'

Jason flung the empty bowl at Varalak's head, then
sprang round and raced back along the path towards
the ruins, fright galvanizing his weary, aching legs. He
reached the clearing – that same clearing where the
Shans had seized them, it seemed, a lifetime ago –
crossed it as if on wings, and at the far side stumbled
to a halt and looked back, panting. There was no sign
of Varalak. Had he gone after Angus or Meg? Oh for
that shotgun, groaned Jason to himself – he *knew* they
shouldn't have dumped it! He stood a moment, wiping

sweat from his eyes and feeling his breath gradually steady, while thoughts tumbled through his mind. He could circle around, perhaps sneak into the hut and telephone, or there was the Border Patrol at the river, if he could get there unseen. He stood undecided – and then Varalak burst into the clearing, two red-rimmed and furious eyes blinking from the grotesque white mask of flour, the pistol in his upraised right hand. Jason turned and forced his legs into a run. At the crash of movement Varalak shouted something but Jason only quickened his unsteady pace. He reached the first blocks of fallen stone and ran between them, looking frantically for somewhere to hide, then just ahead saw the great squat pyramid tomb. He could duck into that and let Varalak go past! He ran along the front of the building, came to the dark doorway, twitched aside the curtain of root tendrils, and started to enter. But suddenly he thought: I'd be trapped in there! Instead he turned aside a few paces and flung himself down behind a heap of masonry on the other side of the path.

The pounding feet followed, then stopped. Jason began to lift himself, ready to make a final dash for it – and saw Varalak looking at the dark doorway and the still gently moving root tendrils. From his pocket Varalak took a cigarette lighter, parted the curtain and sidled in, and Jason saw the glow of the lighter flame inside. He heard a voice call, 'Jason?' The voice was reassuring, friendly even. 'There is no need to be frightened, Jason.' Then there was an exclamation, three rapid shots and the light went out. Varalak came backing out, then turned and ran stumbling back towards the camp. Out from the doorway glided a snake, a huge snake with an olive-green back, an orange throat that seemed to pulsate and glow in the weak forest light, and a fist-sized head from which glittered two unblinking eyes. At the sight of it, Jason leapt back, shaking. What else lurked in these ancient chambers and along these narrow corridors of stone?

Varalak had probably been bitten by that thing – but he still had his pistol, and would certainly use it. Jason clambered warily among the ruins and over the great sprawling roots, listening for sounds of pursuit – then suddenly he heard a voice calling his name, not Varalak's voice, but Bain's, and not far away. 'Jason!' it called, 'Jason – can you hear me?'

'Yes!' His voice cracked and he cleared his throat and roared back, 'Yes, I can hear you.'

'This way – it's all right!'

He began making his way towards the voice, which called at him at intervals, and at last he came out at the central clearing. Bain was there, and Meg, who ran towards him. 'Oh, Jason – when we heard the shots we thought he'd killed you!' To his astonishment he saw fresh tear-stains on her cheek.

'I'm all right,' he said, a little gruffly, but looked round uneasily. 'What happened to Varalak, where'd he go?'

'The Border Patrol have got him, they came running up from the ford when they heard the first shots. But we think he's dying, he can't speak, it looks as if he's been bitten by something, a snake probably.' Up towards the camp huts a jeep roared, but Jason ignored it; the sight of Varalak stumbling away was too fresh and vivid in his mind. 'Yes, he was. I saw it.'

'You *saw* it?' Bain's eyebrows shot up. 'He must have been close!'

Jason shivered. 'He was.' Then he explained. 'That pyramid temple – I thought I'd go in there and hide, then changed my mind; I hid near it, but he thought I'd gone inside and went in after me.'

'That's where the hill people go to perform their ceremonies every full moon,' said Meg, her eyes suddenly sharp and attentive. 'They worship that huge carved Naga over the doorway. That's why we were leaving a study of it for another year or two, we didn't go near it for fear of offending them – but go on. What happened?'

'Varalak went into the doorway and struck his cigarette lighter. I couldn't see inside, but suddenly there were some shots and the light went out. Then he came backing out, and with him' – Jason gulped and looked about – 'with him came a snake about fifteen feet long and as thick as my leg. It went one way and I went the other. Then after a bit I heard you calling.'

'So it wasn't just a carved doorway they worshipped!' Meg drew a deep breath. 'Of course – the prototype of the Naga is the hamadryad, the king cobra, and they exist in Thailand all right.'

Here Bain broke in. 'When I first saw that place I felt something familiar about it, and now I know what it was. I got the same feeling in the snake-house at the zoo – it had the same atmosphere! Do you know, I bet there's a family of them in there!'

'And Varalak has provided their latest sacrifice.'
Meg shivered suddenly.

'Jason!' The shout of welcome came from the
direction of the camp. A bulky figure in shorts and shirt
was running down the path towards them. 'Jason – and
Mr Bain and Miss Lacey! Oh, we were so worried
about you!' Chula seized their hands one after the
other, pumping them up and down and beaming as
Jason had never seen him beam before. How could I
ever have doubted him, thought Jason, seeing the lines
of anxiety and strain around his eyes. 'And Mr Lacey,
where is he?'

'He's dead.' Bain spoke swiftly, holding Chula's
eyes. 'Killed trying to escape. I'll give you the details
later,' and he gave a fractional jerk of the head towards
Meg. Colonel Chula's eyes narrowed but he said softly,
'Of course,' then to Meg, 'I offer my deep condolences.'
She nodded her head in silence, and quickly Chula said,
'My jeep is waiting. Come – you will welcome a drive
after your travels on foot. You must have had a certain
amount of walking to do, I expect?'

'Walking!' Jason blinked, 'Do you know, I think
we've walked' – he made a quick calculation – 'easily
a hundred miles!'

'Hardly a hundred, Jason!' Bain raised an eyebrow.
'That's what it feels like, but – ' Talking busily they
began to walk back along the path to the camp when
Jason saw another figure he recognized hurrying
towards them and saluting Chula. It was the grim-
faced Thai he had last seen in the forest camp.

'You remember Mr Udom, Jason?' said Chula.

With a nod to Jason, Udom spoke to the Colonel and

pointed a little way along the path, where two men of the Border Patrol stood by a covered form on a stretcher. Chula grimaced. 'Mr Varalak is dead – but he is the reason I came. When I heard that he had suddenly driven away from the Rest House I followed.'

'He didn't tell anyone where he was going?' asked Meg.

'No, Miss Lacey, not a word. But we have been watching him for some time. We have also,' he coughed apologetically, 'been watching you and Mr Lacey; we had our suspicions. But now,' he went on more briskly, 'you must bath and change.' His eyes twinkled. 'It is very necessary!'

Bain nodded ruefully. 'You never said a truer word, Colonel.'

'Come then. We will go to the Rest House, and as soon as you are ready we will eat and I will hear all your adventures.'

'What's to happen to me,' asked Meg bluntly. 'Prison?'

'No, not that. You were not a prime mover in this affair, and my Government has no charges against you. We will send you home to your parents, Miss Lacey – I will call you that, although it is not your real name. Mr Lacey was not your brother at all, was he?'

'No.' Her face was expressionless.

'However, all that is past. Now, I have my jeep ready – '

'There's Jenny!' broke in Jason. 'The mule – I promised her a feed, she still hasn't had anything to eat.'

'The mule will be welcomed by the Border Patrol

and she will be well looked after, I promise you.' He turned and gave a brief order to a policeman standing nearby, and the man saluted with a wide smile and hurried off.

'Now,' said Colonel Chula. 'Supper!'

Eastwards over the Mekong the moon rose. In Ban Phao lamps were lit as the shops were shuttered, and groups of villagers gathered to drink cups of rice spirit and gossip over the strange events that had taken place in the old ruins, and about which garbled and exotic versions were emerging from the lips of men of the Border Patrol. In the Rest House at the end of the village Jason, Bain and Meg, unfamiliar in clean clothes and neatly combed hair, sat contemplating the empty plates of the last course of a carefully prepared meal.

'Will you not have a second helping, Jason?' Colonel Chula gazed at him with concern. 'You have not eaten properly for days – you should be able to do better than this!'

Jason shook his head in surprised disappointment. 'I was sure I could have eaten a horse,' he said. 'But I can't swallow another mouthful – I can't think why.'

'Simple,' Angus Bain leant back. 'Your stomach has shrunk. But don't worry,' he added with a faint grin, 'it'll be back in its usual condition by about lunch-time tomorrow.' He yawned and Jason, blinking, yawned with him.

Colonel Chula looked at them in some alarm. 'I was looking forward to hearing from you just what happened,' he said, 'but perhaps you had better sleep first.'

'Oh, we can keep awake,' said Angus. 'A cup of your excellent coffee and we'll tell you the whole story.'

Over steaming cups of coffee Bain explained it all, step by step, to Colonel Chula, who listened without comment though with a start of astonishment at mention of Yasuno, till Angus laid by the Colonel's cup the clear plastic packet of white powder marked with the Globe and Tiger. 'This is what they had.'

Chula sprang up, knocking his chair backwards as he stared at the crudely stencilled blue trademark. 'So that is where it has been coming through!' He seized it. 'This packet explains everything!' He took a deep breath. 'And you say that Yasuno did not get away with very much?' He recovered his chair and sat down again, but his eyes never left Bain's face.

'Very little, if anything at all. I pierced the packets we left in the tins – and you know what damp does to heroin.'

Colonel Chula, the tell-tale packet in front of him, removed the cheroot from his mouth and said reflectively, 'Yasuno and his men no longer dare use paths. The Shans will be anxious to find them – very anxious – and the KMT on the east ridge would also like to get their hands on them. Yasuno and the Haus will have to carry those four tins – what did you say they weighed?'

'About twenty kilos each, say forty-five pounds weight,' said Angus.

'They must carry those loads on their backs through hill forest,' said the Colonel. 'It should take them, I estimate, two days to reach the Mekong. They will find the boat they have hidden, and they will cross by night – that presents no problems.' He took a reflective puff at his cheroot. 'They will want to sell their cargo, as they will not dare try to smuggle it through communist territory.' He took the cheroot from his mouth. 'Now, will you tell me again just what you put in those tins?'

'There was earth, leaf-mould, rotten wood – '

'And white ants!' broke in Jason. 'Don't forget the white ants!'

'Let us visualize the scene,' mused Chula. 'Yasuno will contact the communists. They will be suspicious of a stranger, especially a Japanese, but will certainly meet him. He will ask a high price for his wares, and they will haggle. Each side will be very watchful, and you may be sure that there will be plenty of guns about.' Colonel Chula paused and Jason, holding his breath, could see that he was savouring the scene in his mind. His sleepy eyes half-shut over his cigar and a faint smile on his lips, Chula went on, 'They will eventually agree on a price and money will be produced, probably in American greenbacks.'

'Go on, Colonel!' Jason was hugging himself.

'This money will be held up before Yasuno, but he will not be given it. The North Vietnamese, like communists everywhere, have suspicious natures, for they assume that other people are like themselves. They will invite Yasuno to show all his goods.' Colonel Chula again removed the cheroot from his lips with fingers that shook slightly. 'Then,' he went on carefully, 'Yasuno and his men will proudly open the tins and they will empty out the contents on to the table before them.'

His belly started to shake, he put down his cigar and

wiped his eyes, then looked up again. For a moment the four of them sat looking at each other in absolute silence.

In the street outside two villagers sat with their cheroots and their cups of rice spirit in the moonlight. They were talking in low voices, still turning over the events of the day, when suddenly their talk was interrupted. From the Rest House came a great, convulsive shout of laughter, a roar of laughter that went on and on in gusts of joyous sound. On it went till the villagers looked at each other uneasily, and one confided to the other, 'The spirits of the old temple must have taken possession of the White people.'

His companion listened, head cocked, but as the laughter sank into breathless gasps of pure enjoyment he demurred. 'Not so. It is rumoured that the Spirit of the Naga received an important sacrifice today, and so looks with favour upon the White strangers. That is not the noise of men possessed by demons. No.' He lifted his cup of rice spirit and listened again as a fresh burst of laughter broke out. 'No,' he repeated. 'They make these noises because' – with a swift movement he tossed back his fiery drink – 'because they are happy.'